D1462986

BLUE BOOK OF UNITED STATES COINS

1964

HANDBOOK

OF

UNITED STATES COINS

With Premium List

TWENTY-FIRST EDITION

By R. S. YEOMAN

Containing mint record and prices paid by dealers for all U. S. coins. Information on collecting coins — how coins are produced—mints and mint marks—grading of coins—location of mint marks—preserving and cleaning coins—starting a collection—what to buy—history of mints and interesting descriptions of all U.S. copper, nickel, silver and gold coins. Fully illustrated. INDEX PAGE 126.

© *Copyright, 1963, by*

WHITMAN PUBLISHING COMPANY

RACINE, WISCONSIN

9050   Printed in U.S.A. by Western Printing and Lithographing Co.

Foreword

During the past few years there has been a remarkable new interest in coin collecting. Thousands of people are forming sets of dates and mint marks of common cents, nickels, dimes, and other available United States coins in Whitman Coin Folders. There has been a persistent demand for a practical guide book offering general information about coins, reduced to simple everyday language.

This volume offers a helping hand to the new collector; explains what he should collect and what he should discard; tells him how to appraise and care for his coins. The simplest explanations are employed here, so that the reader may easily derive the utmost in enjoyment and profit from a collection of even the most common coins taken from ordinary pocket change.

While the primary purpose of this volume is to smooth the path toward numismatics for the beginner, much of the information, such as mint records, premium prices, varieties, and the like, will prove an invaluable aid to the more advanced collector.

The premium list gives representative prices paid by dealers for various United States coins. These prices have been assembled from many widely separated sources, and are averages. Slight differences in prices among dealers on some issues depend on proximity to the various mints and populous centers. Other factors, such as local supply and demand, may also tend to raise or lower prices from those listed in this book. Uncirculated and proof coins bring premium prices for many coins, though they bring no premium when circulated.

The publishers welcome suggestions and criticisms from readers. It is hoped that this volume will provide a practical introduction to numismatics as well as a handy reference book for the average collector of coins.

CONTRIBUTORS

Lee F. Hewitt, the well-known editor and publisher of the NUMISMATIC SCRAPBOOK MAGAZINE, was an early contributor having supplied many of the historical references and explanations which appear throughout this book.

The late Charles E. Green gave valuable counsel when the first edition of the HANDBOOK was undertaken. He supplied most of the mint data, and was a regular contributor to each revised edition until his untimely death in late 1955.

CONTRIBUTORS TO THE TWENTY-FIRST EDITION

Kenneth E. Bressett — *Co-ordinating Editor*

A. E. Bebee	Garland Hughes	Neil Shafer
Hy Brown	A. M. Kagin	Norman Shultz
Malcolm O. E. Chell-Frost	Paul Kagin	Leonard W. Stark
Jerry Cohen	Abner Kreisberg	Maurice A. Storck
Carl Curcio	Ken Lee	Don Thompson
B. M. Douglas	Franklyn H. Miller	R. E. Wallace
Ben Dreiske	Earl A. Parker	Tom Warfield
Darvin France	Hubert L. Polzer	Frank Washburn
Bernard Gimelson	Elmer Ray	Harold Whiteneck

Important Notice————

THIS BOOK IS *NOT A RETAIL PRICE LIST*

Premium prices are the average amount dealers will pay for coins (according to condition) if required for their stock.

(See page 14)

The GUIDE BOOK of UNITED STATES COINS ($1.75) furnishes collectors and dealers with retail valuations.

Whitman Coin Folders are described on page 127.

Brief guides to grading are placed before each major coin type in this book. For those readers who desire more detailed descriptions of all coin grades, we recommend A GUIDE TO THE GRADING OF UNITED STATES COINS by Martin R. Brown and John W. Dunn.

IF YOU HAVE COINS TO SELL

The publishers are not engaged in the rare coin business; however, the chances are that the dealer from whom you purchased this book is engaged in the buying and selling of rare coins — contact him first. In the event that you purchased this book from a source other than a numismatic establishment, consult your local telephone directory for the names of coin dealers (they will be frequently found under the heading of "Stamp and Coin Dealers"). If you live in a city or town that does not have any coin dealers, it is suggested that you obtain a copy of one of the trade publications, in order to obtain the names and addresses of many of the country's leading dealers.

At the present time there are several popular magazines and papers that are devoted to coin collecting:

The Numismatist
(Published monthly by
the American Numismatic
Association.)
3520 North 7th Street
Phoenix 14, Arizona
(Single Copy 50¢)

Coins Magazine (Monthly)
Iola, Wisconsin
(Single Copy 35¢)

Numismatic News (Every other week)
Iola, Wisconsin
(Single Copy 20¢)

Coin World (Weekly)
Sidney News Building
Sidney, Ohio
(Single Copy 25¢)

Hobbies Magazine (Monthly)
1006 S. Michigan
Chicago, Illinois
(Has a coin section, Single copy 35¢)

Numismatic Scrapbook Magazine
(Monthly)
7320 N. Milwaukee Ave.
Chicago, Illinois
(Single Copy 50¢)

COLLECTING COINS

Numismatics or coin collecting is one of the world's oldest hobbies, dating back several centuries. Coin collecting in America did not develop to any extent until about 1840 as our pioneer forefathers were too busy carving a country out of wilderness to afford the luxury of a hobby. The discontinuance of the large-sized cent in 1857 caused many persons to attempt to accumulate a complete set of the pieces while they were still in circulation. One of the first groups of collectors to band together for the study of numismatics was the Numismatic and Antiquarian Society of Philadelphia, organized on January 1, 1858. Lack of an economical method to house a collection held the number of devotees to coin collecting to a few thousand until the Whitman Publishing Company and other manufacturers placed the low-priced coin boards and folders on the market some years ago. Since that time the number of Americans collecting coins has increased many-fold.

The Production of Coins

To collect coins intelligently it is necessary to have some knowledge of the manner in which our coins are produced. They are made in factories called "mints." The Mint of the United States was established at Philadelphia by a resolution of Congress dated April 2, 1792. The Act also provided for the coinage of gold eagles ($10), half-eagles and quarter-eagles, the silver dollar, half-dollar, quarter-dollar, dime (originally spelled "disme") and the half-disme or half-dime; the copper cent and half-cent. According to the Treasury Department, the first coins struck were one-cent and half-cent pieces, in March of 1793 on a hand-operated press. Most numismatic authorities consider the half-disme of 1792 as the first United States coinage, quoting the words of George Washington as their authority; Washington, in his annual address, November 6, 1792, having said, "There has been a small beginning in the coining of the Half-Dimes, the want of small coins in circulation calling the first attention to them." In the museum of Congress Hall, Philadelphia, are exhibited a number of implements, etc., from the original mint, and some coins discovered when the old building was wrecked. These coins included half-dismes, and the placard identifying them states that Washington furnished the silver and gave the coined pieces to his friends as souvenirs.

Prior to the adoption of the Constitution, the Continental Congress arranged for the issuance of copper coins under private contract. These are known as the "Fugio cents" from the design of the piece, which shows a sun-dial and the Latin word "fugio" — "I Fly" or, in connection with the sundial, "Time Flies." The ever appropriate motto, "Mind Your Business," is also on the coin.

In the manufacture of a given coin the first step is the cutting of the "die." Prior to the latter part of the nineteenth century dies for United States coins were "cut by hand." Briefly this method is as follows: The design having been determined, a drawing the exact size of the coin is made. A tracing is made from this drawing. A piece of steel is smoothed and coated with transfer wax, and the tracing impressed into the wax. The engraver then tools out the steel where the relief or raised effect is required. If the design is such that it can all be produced by cutting away steel, the die is hardened and ready for use. Some dies are not brought to a finished state, as some part of the design can perhaps be done better in relief. In that case, when all that can be accomplished to advantage in the die is completed, it is hardened, a soft-steel impression is taken from it, and the unfinished parts are then completed. This piece of steel is in turn hardened and, by a press, driven into another piece of soft-steel, thus making a die which, when hardened, is ready for the making of coins.

This hand method of cutting dies accounts for the many die varieties of early United States coins. Where the amount of coinage of a given year was large enough to wear out several dies, each new die placed in the coining press created another die variety of that year. The dies being cut by hand, no two were exactly alike in every detail. Of the cents dated 1794 over sixty different die varieties have been discovered.

Hundreds of dies are now used by the mints of the United States each year, but they are all made from one master die, which is produced in the following manner:

After the design is settled upon, the plaster of Paris or wax model is prepared several times the actual size of the coin. When this model is finished an electrotype (an exact duplicate in metal) is made and prepared for the reducing lathe. The reducing lathe is a machine, working on the principle of the pantograph, only in this case the one point traces or follows the form of the model while another and much smaller point in the form of a drill cuts away the steel and produces a reduced size die of the model. The die is finished and details are sharpened or worked over by an engraver with chisel and graver. The master die is used to make duplicates in soft-steel which are then hardened and ready for the coining press. To harden dies, they are placed in cast-iron boxes packed with carbon to exclude the air, and when heated to a bright red are cooled suddenly with water.

In the coinage operations the first step is to prepare the alloy. The alloys now used are: silver coins, 90% silver and 10% copper; five-cent pieces, 75% copper and 25% nickel; one-cent pieces, 95% copper and 5% zinc. (The 1943 cent consists of steel coated with zinc; and the five-cent piece 1942-1945 contains 35% silver, 56% copper and 9% manganese.) The alloy is melted in crucibles and poured into molds to form ingots. The ingots are in the form of thin bars and vary in size according to the denomination of the coin. The width is sufficient to allow three coins to be cut from the strips.

The ingots are next put through rolling mills to reduce the thickness to required limits. The strips are then fed into cutting presses which cut circular blanks (planchets) of the approximate size of the finished coin. The blanks are run through annealing furnaces to soften them; next through tumbling barrels, rotating cylinders containing cleaning solutions which clean and burnish the metal, and finally into centrifugal drying machines.

The blanks are next fed into a milling machine which produces the raised or upset rim. The blank is now ready for the coining press.

The blank is held firmly by a collar, as it is struck, under heavy pressure varying from 40 tons for the one-cent pieces and dimes, to 170 tons for silver dollars. Upper and lower dies impress the design on both sides of the coin. The pressure is sufficient to produce a raised surface level with those of the milled rim. The collar holding the blank for silver coins is grooved. The pressure forces the metal into the grooves of the collar, producing the "reeding" on the finished coin.

How a Proof Coin Is Made

Metal blanks are carefully selected. Those without scratches or other imperfections are washed with a solution of Cream of Tartar. After rinsing in water they are dipped in alcohol.

The dies for making proofs receive a special polish resulting in a mirror-like surface not unlike the finished brilliant proof coin. Unlike ordinary coinage produced by mechanical pressure at the rate of 90 to 130 coins per minute, proof coins are struck by hydraulic pressure at a slower rate. Small details such as delicate hair lines are brought out in clear-cut relief by this method. The coins are carefully handled and are never allowed to come in contact with other coins.

Certain coins including Lincoln cents, Buffalo nickels, Quarter Eagles, Half Eagles, Eagles and Double Eagles between the years 1908 and 1916 were made with a matte or sandblast surface. Matte proofs have a dull frosted surface which is produced by special treatment after striking.

Mints and Mint Marks

In addition to the Philadelphia Mint, the U. S. Government has from time to time established branch mints in various parts of the country. At the present time a branch mint operates in Denver. The Denver Mint has operated since 1906. A mint was operated at New Orleans from 1838 to 1861 and again from 1879 to 1909. Mints were also in service at Carson City, Nevada, from 1870 to 1893; at Charlotte, North Carolina, from 1838 to 1861; at Dahlonega, Georgia, from 1838 to 1861; and at San Francisco from 1854 to 1955.

Coins struck at Philadelphia (excepting 1942 to 1945 five-cent pieces) do not carry a mint mark. The mint mark is found only on coins struck at the branch mints. It is a small letter, usually found on the reverse side (the Lincoln cent is one exception to the rule; there are other exceptions, too). The letters to signify the various mints are as follows:

"C" for Charlotte, North Carolina (on gold coins only).

"CC" for Carson City, Nevada.

"D" for Dahlonega, Georgia (gold coins only, 1838 to 1861).

"D" for Denver, Colorado (from 1906 to date).

"O" for New Orleans, Louisiana.

"P" for Philadelphia, Pennsylvania.

"S" for San Francisco, California.

The mint mark is of utmost importance to collectors due to the fact that the coinage at the branch mints has usually been much smaller than at Philadelphia and many of the branch mint pieces are very scarce.

Location of Mint Marks

Half Cents — All coined at Philadelphia, no mint mark.

Large Cents — All coined at Philadelphia, no mint mark.

Flying Eagle Cents — All coined at Philadelphia, no mint mark.

Indian Cents — 1908 and 1909, under the wreath on reverse side.

Lincoln Cents — Under the date.

Two Cents, Three Cent Nickels — All coined at Philadelphia, no mint mark.

Three Cents Silver — All coined at Philadelphia, except 1851 New Orleans mint — reverse side.

Shield Nickels — All coined at Philadelphia, no mint mark.

Liberty Nickels — All coined at Philadelphia except 1912 S and D — reverse side to left of word CENTS.

Buffalo Nickels — Reverse side under words FIVE CENTS.

Jefferson Nickels — Reverse side at right of the building.

Jefferson Five-Cent Pieces (silver, 1942-1945 inclusive) — Above dome on reverse.

Half Dimes — Reverse side either within or below the wreath.

Dimes — Old types on reverse side below or within wreath; Mercury type (1916 to date) on the reverse to left of the fasces. Roosevelt type starting 1946, at left of base of torch.

Twenty Cents — Reverse, under the eagle.

Quarter Dollars — Old types on reverse under eagle; Standing Liberty type (after 1916) obverse to left of date; Washington type on reverse under eagle.

Half Dollars — 1838 and 1839 O mint mark over date; other dates to 1915 on reverse under eagle. 1917 comes with mints S and D on obverse and reverse. After 1917 on lower left reverse. Franklin, above liberty bell beam.

Dollars — Old types, on reverse under eagle; Peace type (1921 and after) on reverse near eagle's wing.

Trade Dollars — On reverse under eagle.

Gold Dollars — Reverse under wreath.

Quarter Eagles ($2.50) — 1838 and 1839 over the date; other dates previous to 1907 on reverse under the eagle; Indian type (1908-29) on reverse lower left.

Three Dollar Pieces — Reverse under the wreath.

Half Eagles ($5.00) — Same as quarter eagles.

Eagles ($10.00) — Reverse under eagle; after 1907 at left of value.

Double Eagles ($20.00) — Old types on reverse under eagle; St. Gaudens (after 1907) above the date.

MINT MARKS

1908 and 1909 Indian Cents. San Francisco Mint only.

S or D found below date on obverse of Lincoln Cents.

Three-cent Silver, 1851 is only date this denomination produced at a branch mint. (New Orleans.)

[8]

Liberty Head Nickel 1912 S and D only, on reverse side.

Buffalo Nickel, on reverse side under "FIVE CENTS."

Jefferson Nickel, on reverse at right of building.

Jefferson 5c Silver 1942 to 1945. Above dome on reverse side.

Half-dime, within wreath, reverse side.

Half-dime, below wreath, reverse side.

(1871-72 have mint marks below or within wreath.)

Dime—old type. Reverse side. 1872-75-76 etc. have mint mark within wreath also, as shown for half-dimes.

Barber Dime. Below wreath, reverse side.

Mercury Dime. On reverse to left of the fasces.

Roosevelt Dime

Twenty-cent Piece. On reverse, under Eagle.

Quarter — old type. On reverse, under Eagle.

Barber Quarter. On reverse, under Eagle.

Standing Liberty Quarter. Very small mint mark found on obverse at left of date.

MINT MARKS

Washington Quarter. On reverse, under Eagle.

Half Dollar 1838-0. On obverse, above date. (See page 64.)

Half Dollar, Barber and earlier types. On reverse, under Eagle.

Standing Liberty Half Dollar. 1916-1917 on obverse.

Standing Liberty Half Dollar. 1917 and later dates on reverse. (Both obverse and reverse on 1917.)

Franklin Half Dollar. Above liberty bell beam.

Silver Dollar—old types. On reverse, under Eagle.

Peace Type Dollar. On reverse, tip of eagle's wing.

Trade Dollar. On reverse, under Eagle.

Gold Dollar. On reverse, under wreath.

Quarter Eagle. 1838 and 1839 over date.

Quarter Eagle. On reverse under eagle until 1879.

Quarter Eagle—Indian Type. On reverse, lower left.

Three-Dollar Gold. On reverse under wreath.

Eagle—old types. On reverse, under eagle.

Half Eagles. Mint marks found in the same position as Quarter Eagles.

[10]

MINT MARKS

Eagle — After 1907. At
left of value.

Double Eagle—old types.
On reverse under Eagle.

Double Eagle — After
1907. Above date.

DISTINGUISHING MARKS

The illustrations and explanations in this section will help the collector to identify certain well-known varieties.

HALF CENTS OF 1795-1796
SHOWING LOCATION OF POLE
TO CAP

The end of the staff, or pole lies parallel with the line of the bust, which is pointed. The die-maker, probably through error, omitted the pole on some of the dies of 1795 and 1796.

Pole to Cap

No Pole to Cap

Stemless Wreath

Stems to Wreath

STEMLESS WREATH VARIETY OF
HALF CENTS AND LARGE CENTS

Observe the reverse side for this variety. Illustrations at left show both stemless and stems to wreath types for easy comparison—stemless wreath found on 1804, 1805, 1806, Half cents. 1797, 1802, 1803 Large cents.

1804 HALF CENT PROTRUDING
TONGUE OR SPIKED CHIN VARIETY

Plain 4

Crosslet 4

Details showing differences in 1804 plain 4 and crosslet 4. Note serif on horizontal bar of figure 4 as shown at right.

DISTINGUISHING MARKS

THE 1856 FLYING EAGLE CENT

Collectors are advised to inspect any 1856 Flying Eagle cent carefully.

A few tests will aid in establishing genuineness of this cent, as follows:

THE DATE

The 6 in the date should be as illustrated. If the lower half is thick, it is probably an altered 1858. A magnifying glass will often reveal poor workmanship.

The figure 5 slants slightly to the right on a genuine 1856. The verticle bar points to the center of the ball just beneath. On the 1858, this bar points *outside* the ball. (Compare the two illustrations.)

THE LEGEND

The center of the O in OF is crude and almost squared on the genuine 1856, but on the large letter 1858 it is rounded.

The letters A and M in America are joined in both the 1856 and large letter 1858, but they join at a slight angle on the 1856, while the bottom of the letters form a smooth curve on the 1858 large letter cent.

Large Letters

Small Letters

1858 FLYING EAGLE CENT

Letters A and M in the word AMERICA are joined on the LARGE LETTER variety. They are separated on the SMALL LETTER variety.

DISTINGUISHING MARKS

1864 BRONZE INDIAN HEAD CENT WITH "L" ON RIBBON

Only a very fine or uncirculated specimen will show this small initial. If the coin is turned slightly (so Indian faces observer) the highlighted details of the "L" will appear to better advantage. The point of the bust is pointed on the variety with "L"; rounded without "L." The "L" is the initial of the engraver, Longacre.

Small Motto

Large Motto

TWO CENTS OF 1864

Details explain the differences in these two well-known varieties. Observe the D in God, it is narrow on the large motto. The stem to the leaf shows plainly on the small motto variety. There is no stem on the large motto coin. First T in TRUST, small motto variety, is closer to ribbon crease at left.

(At top) 1909 Initials appear on reverse. (At right) Initials appear beneath shoulder, 1918 and later.

LINCOLN CENTS SHOWING LOCATION OF INITIALS V D B

1918-S QUARTER 8 OVER 7

A variety of this kind is rarely found in coinage of the twentieth century.

[13]

DISTINGUISHING MARKS

1938D over S Nickel Variety

1955 Cent
Double Die Obverse

Large Date Cent
1960

Small Date Cent
1960

1942 Over 41 Dime
Philadelphia Mint

CONDITION OF COINS

FAIR. Coin has sufficient design and letters to be easily identified. Excessive wear.

G. or GOOD. All of design, every feature and legend must be plain and date clear.

V. G. or VERY GOOD. Features all clear and bold. Better than good, but not quite fine.

F. or FINE. Obviously a circulated coin but little wear. Mint lustre gone. All letters in LIBERTY and mottoes clear.

V. FINE or VERY FINE. Shows enough wear on high spots to be noticable. Still retains enough lustre to be desirable.

EX. FINE or EXTREMELY FINE. Slightly circulated with some lustre but faint evidence of wear.

UNC. or UNCIRCULATED. New. Regular mint striking, but never placed in circulation. Older pieces may be tarnished or "toned."

PF. or PROOF. Coins with mirror-like surface, specially struck for collectors at Philadelphia only. Also sandblast and matte proof. *See Page 7.*

Coins from Branch mints having a mirror-like surface are not proofs but are first strikings of new dies.

IMPORTANT: Coins in any condition with defects, such as those which are bent, corroded, scratched, holed, nicked, stained, oxidized, mutilated, or have other imperfections are worth less than if free of these defects.

Preserving and Cleaning Coins

Most numismatists will tell you to "never clean a coin" and it is good advice; however, every collector tries to clean a coin sooner or later, so we are passing on a few tips here.

In the first place some effort should be made to keep uncirculated and proof coins bright so they won't need cleaning. Tarnish on a coin is purely a chemical process caused by oxygen in the air acting on the metal or by chemicals with which the coin comes in contact. One of the commonest chemicals causing tarnish is sulphur; most paper, with the exception of specially manufactured "sulphur-free" kinds, contains sulphur due to the sulphuric acid that is used in paper manufacture. Therefore do not wrap coins in ordinary paper; also keep uncirculated and proof coins away from rubber bands (lay a rubber band on a silver coin for a few days and then note the "black stripe" on the coin where the band touched).

The utmost in protection is received by wrapping the coin in lead or aluminum foil and then placing it in a tarnish-proof envelope (both items are sold by coin dealers).

Many coins become marred by careless handling. Always hold the coin by the edge. The accompanying illustration shows the right and wrong way to handle numismatic specimens. It is a breach of numismatic etiquette to handle another collector's coin except by the edge, even if it is not an uncirculated or proof piece.

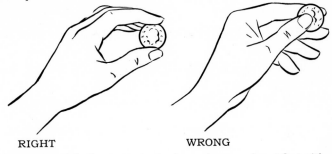

RIGHT   WRONG

If you must satisfy the urge to try to clean coins, experiment first with some ordinary coins.

Modern silver coins can often be cleaned with a paste consisting of baking soda and water without harming the coin. Hold about a teaspoonful of paste in the palm of one hand. Work the coin gently into the paste with the other hand. Rinse the coin in clear water and dry with a clean blotter. Do not use kitchen cleanser or other abrasives on any coins.

Copper and bronze coins are very difficult to clean. Scrubbing with an abrasive makes the high parts of the coin bright while the other parts will look dirtier than ever, giving the piece a very unnatural appearance that considerably lessens its value in the numismatic market. The use of acids and buffing wheels also produces an unnatural appearance.

No amount of scrubbing or cleaning, or the use of acids or buffers, will restore the original mint lustre to a coin.

Starting a Collection

One may start a collection of United States coins with very little expense by systematically assembling the various dates and mint marks of all the types and denominations that are now in general circulation. Whitman's coin folders make this possible.

With the exception of the thirty-five cents paid for the coin folder, collecting the coins that are received in the ordinary daily business transactions entails no expense whatever; a buffalo nickel, for example, that has been taken out of circulation can always be spent for 5 cents if the occasion arrives. Filling a board or two out of circulation is probably the best method of determining whether coin collecting appeals to you. Not everyone can be a successful coin collector. It requires patience, intelligence of a high order, and a certain desire to know the meaning behind a lot of things that at first glance and to the ordinary mortal appear meaningless. You may not be cut out to be a collector but you'll never know until you look further into the subject, and if by the time a board or two of coins are collected you have no burning desire to acquire many more different coins, you will probably never be a collector. However, the chances are that you will be, because if you have read this far in this book it shows that you are interested in the subject.

While starting a collection by the "out-of-circulation" method is the least expensive method, it is possible to not only have a lot of fun with such a collection but also to profit to a certain degree. The cheapest coins to collect are the current Lincoln head cents. All dates can be found in circulation. There are scores of coins dated after 1900 that are in circulation and worth a premium to collectors. It is possible to collect about 500 different United States coins out of general circulation. Such a collection in fine or better condition could be sold for considerably more than the face value.

Perfection is the goal of every endeavor and coin collecting is no exception. After a board has been filled with circulated specimens the next step will be to replace pieces with coins in uncirculated condition; or perhaps to start collecting the obsolete series; in either case it will be necessary to purchase some coins from dealers or other collectors. The most logical way to keep abreast with the market, or obtain the addresses of the country's leading dealers, is to subscribe to one or more of the trade publications (see page 5 for list of the coin magazines). These magazines carry advertisements of various dealers listing coins for sale. Moreover, through this source the beginner may obtain price lists and catalogs from the dealers.

There are several good reference books available at reasonable prices which will be helpful to the collector who wishes to know more about U. S. coins and paper money. The GUIDE BOOK OF U. S. COINS (Red Book) is an expanded version of THE HANDBOOK. It lists retail values of all regular U. S. coins and also lists all coins of the U. S. Colonial period and private and territorial gold coins.

Most coin shops, book stores and hobby dealers can supply the following titles:

GUIDE BOOK OF U. S COINS — Yeoman
U. S COMMEMORATIVE COINAGE — Slabaugh
SELECTIONS FROM THE NUMISMATIST, Vol. I — U. S. COINS
U. S. PATTERN, EXPERIMENTAL & TRIAL PIECES — Judd
PATRIOTIC CIVIL WAR TOKENS — Fuld
GUIDE TO CIVIL WAR STORE CARDS — Fuld
THE FANTASTIC 1804 DOLLAR — Newman & Bressett
CONFEDERATE STATES PAPER MONEY — Slabaugh
THE STORY OF PAPER MONEY — Reinfeld

JOIN A COIN CLUB

A beginner should join a "coin club" if he is fortunate enough to live in a city which has one. The association with more experienced collectors will be of great benefit. Practically all the larger cities have one or more clubs and they are being rapidly organized in the smaller towns. The publications mentioned on page 5 carry lists of coin clubs and special events such as coin shows and conventions.

Abbreviations

Like most businesses the coin trade has developed a number of abbreviations which are used generally in magazine advertising to conserve space in listing coins. To many a beginner, reading such an advertisement for the first time, it is difficult to understand. However, the abbreviations are not numerous and they can be quickly mastered. Some of the abbreviations are peculiar to particular types or denominations and are mentioned in this book in their respective places. The more general abbreviations are:

Obv. or Ob. — Obverse. The "heads" side of a coin.

Rev., Rx., or R. — Reverse. The "tails" side of a coin.

Var., Vars. — Variety, Varieties.

Ty. or T. — Type. (A frequent abbreviation is O.T. or N.T., meaning new type or old type.)

Lib. — Liberty.

Lge. or Lg. — Large.

Sm. — Small.

The condition of the coin is the most frequently abbreviated item. The common condition abbreviations are:

Pr. or Pf. — Proof.

Unc., Uncir., or U. — Uncirculated.

E.F., X.F., or ExF. — Extremely Fine. (Also Extra Fine.)

V.F. — Very Fine. (The "V" is sometimes used to denote "very" in other cases, such as very rare, very scarce.)

V.G. or V.Gd. — Very Good.

G. or Gd. — Good.

Fr. — Fair.

Brill., or Bril. — Brilliant.

An example of an abbreviated coin listing is as follows:

Standing Liberty Quarters
1917-S Var. 2, VG, Sc........$0.00

The figures "1917" stand for the year of coinage, "S" for the San Francisco mint mark, "Var. 2" means the piece is of the second variety, "VG" is the condition, "Sc." meaning the piece is scarce. The price which follows is the value of the coin.

UNITED STATES PAPER MONEY

Paper money issued by the United States government is collected widely in this country. The first issue of "greenbacks" was made in 1861; paper money was not issued by our government for circulation prior to that date. Collectors of U.S. notes prefer them in crisp, new condition; therefore the old style large-sized notes are seldom saleable unless in new condition.

Before the issuance of the first U.S. paper money, the banks throughout the country issued their own currency. These issues are commonly referred to as "broken bank notes" although that is somewhat of a misnomer as many of the banks did not go broke (a few are still in existence) and redeemed their paper money issues. There are thousands of varieties of these notes in existence most of which are very common and worth from 1¢ to 10¢ each. Before and during the American Revolution the various individual states and the Continental Congress issued paper money. The commoner varieties of these Colonial notes are worth from 10¢ to 50¢; a few are quite rare.

U. S. HALF CENTS

(First year of coinage, 1793; last year of coinage, 1857.)

Metal: Copper.

All half cents are really scarce, but the series has never enjoyed the popularity of some of the other series, hence the more common dates of half cents are reasonably priced.

The series does, however, contain a number of rarities, 1796 being the rarest date. The dates 1840, 1841, 1842, 1843, 1844, 1845, 1846, 1847, 1848, 1849 small date, and 1852 were issued in proof only, and in two varieties. Those with the ten large berries and one small berry on the reverse are called the "originals" and those with eleven small berries on the reverse are termed "restrikes." A restrike is an impression made from genuine dies but at a later time than the date shown on the coin. It is said that eighteen specimens of both varieties of the above mentioned dates were struck.

Terms used in describing Half Cents:

Lettered Edge (1793, 1794, 1795, and 1797) — The words "Two Hundred for a Dollar" are found on the edge of some or all varieties of these dates.

Pole to Cap (or no pole to cap) — All varieties of the 1794 have a "pole to cap," that is, the pole shows beside the head of Liberty. The years 1795 and 1796 are found with the pole and also "without" a pole.

Stemless Wreath; Stems to Wreath — (1804, 1805, and 1806.) On some of the reverses of these dates the wreath has stems; on others the wreath does not have stems. (See page 11.)

Crosslet 4; Plain 4 — On those of 1804 only. The "4" in the date appears on some varieties with a serif; that is known as the "crosslet 4." The variety without serif is known as the "plain 4." There is also a variety of the 1804 known as the "spiked chin" or "protruding tongue" on which Liberty appears to be sticking out her tongue. (See page 11.)

Over-Date — An over-date is the result of using a die of a previous year and re-cutting the new date over the old figures. In the half cent series, the following over-dates are found: 1802 over 1800; 1808 over 7; 1809 over 6. A variety of 1797 has a "1 over 1" which is probably not an over-date but an error in die cutting — the engraver rather than cut a new die merely cut another figure 1.

The following abbreviations are found in numismatic literature referring to half cents.

Pl. — plain; *Let.* — lettered; *Ed.* — edge; *Perf.* — perfect; *Ov.* — over; *Sm.* — small; *Lg.* — large.

Fair — Clear enough to identify.

Good — Outline of bust clear, no details. Date readable. Reverse lettering incomplete.

Very Good — Some hair details. Reverse lettering complete.

Fine — Most of hair detail shows.

	Quan. Minted	Fair	Good	V. Good	Fine
1793............................	31,934	$35.00	$72.50	$100.00	$150.00

HALF CENTS

	Quan. Minted	Fair	Good	V. Good	Fine
1794	81,600	$11.00	$27.50	$35.00	$50.00
1795	25,600	10.00	22.50	27.50	35.00
1796 All kinds	115,480				
Pole to cap, plain edge		117.50	225.00	325.00	610.00
No pole to cap, plain edge		170.00	350.00	525.00	775.00
1797 All kinds	107,048				
Plain edge		8.00	21.00	30.00	47.50
Lettered edge		50.00	85.00	115.00	165.00

Fair — Clear enough to identify.

Good — Bust outline clear, no details, date readable. Reverse lettering worn and incomplete.

Very Good — Some drapery shows. Date and legends complete.

Fine — Shoulder drapery and hair over brow worn smooth.

		Fair	Good	V. Good	Fine
1800	211,530		4.50	6.50	10.00
1802	14,366	17.50	37.50	52.50	87.50
1803	97,900		4.00	5.75	8.75
1804	1,055,312		3.00	3.50	5.50
1805	814,464		3.25	5.00	7.75
1806	356,000		3.00	4.25	6.25
1807	476,000		3.25	4.75	7.00
1808 All kinds	400,000				
8 over 7		8.25	14.00	25.00	35.00
Perfect date			3.50	5.50	8.00

Good — LIBERTY only partly visible on hair band. Lettering, date, stars, worn but visible.

Very Good — LIBERTY entirely visible on hair band. Lower curls worn.

Fine — Only part wear on LIBERTY and hair at top worn in spots.

		Good	V. Good	Fine
1809 All kinds	1,154,572			
Over-date. (9 over 6)		3.75	5.25	8.00
Perfect date		3.00	4.00	5.00

HALF CENTS

	Quan. Minted	Good	V. Good	Fine
1810	215,000	$ 5.00	$ 8.25	$12.50
1811	63,140	19.00	27.50	40.00
1825	63,000	2.75	3.50	5.00
1826	234,000	2.50	3.25	4.75
1828	606,000	2.25	3.00	4.50
1829	487,000	2.50	3.25	4.75
1831 *Original, Proof only	2,200			
(Large berries on wreath)			Proof	300.00
Restrike, Proof only				
(Small berries on wreath)			Proof	250.00

		Good	V. Good	Fine
1832	154,000	2.75	3.75	6.00
(The Director of the Mint does not give the quantity coined; this figure is usually accepted as correct.)				
1833 Accepted quantity coined	120,000	2.25	3.50	6.00
(Director's report shows 154,000)				
1834 Accepted quantity coined	141,000	2.25	3.50	6.00
(Director's report shows 120,000)				
1835 Accepted quantity coined	398,000	2.25	3.50	6.00
(Director's report, 141,000)				
1836 (Director's report, 398,000)				
Original, Proof only			Proof	235.00
(Large berries on wreath)				
Restrike, Proof only			Proof	225.00
(Small berries on wreath)				

Due to the rarity of Half Cents of 1836, and the abundant supply of those dated 1835, it is believed that the Half Cents of 1832, 1833, 1834, 1835, and 1836 were incorrectly reported.

	Good	V. Good	Fine
1837 Token	7.50	10.50	19.00

	Proof
1840 Original, Proof only	225.00
(Large berries on wreath)	
Restrike, Proof only	225.00
(Small berries on wreath)	
1841 Original, Proof only	225.00
(Large berries on wreath)	
Restrike, Proof only	225.00
(Small berries on wreath)	
1842 Original, Proof only	225.00
(Large berries on wreath)	
Restrike, Proof only	225.00
(Small berries on wreath)	
1843 Original, Proof only	225.00
(Large berries on wreath)	
Restrike, Proof only	225.00
(Small berries on wreath)	
1844 Original, Proof only	225.00
(Large berries on wreath)	
Restrike, Proof only	225.00
(Small berries on wreath)	

HALF CENTS

	Proof
1845 Original, Proof only....................................	$225.00
(Large berries on wreath)	
Restrike, Proof only...................................	225.00
(Small berries on wreath)	
1846 Original, Proof only....................................	225.00
(Large berries on wreath)	
Restrike, Proof only...................................	225.00
(Small berries on wreath)	
1847 Original, Proof only....................................	225.00
(Large berries on wreath)	
Restrike, Proof only...................................	225.00
(Small berries on wreath)	
1848 Original, Proof only....................................	225.00
(Large berries on wreath)	
Restrike, Proof only...................................	225.00
(Small berries on wreath)	
1849 Small date. Original, Proof only..........................	225.00
(Large berries on wreath)	
Small date. Restrike, Proof only..........................	225.00
(Small berries on wreath)	

Good — Some of LIBERTY shows and beads partly distinct.
Very Good — Beads uniformly distinct. Hairlines show in spots.
Fine — Hairlines above ear worn. Beads sharp.

	Quan. Minted	Good	V. Good	Fine
1849 Large date.......................39,864		4.50	6.25	11.50
1850.................................39,812		2.75	4.25	6.50
1851.................................147,672		2.25	2.75	4.50

	Proof
1852 Original, Proof only	
(Large berries on wreath)............................	
Restrike, Proof only...................................	225.00
(Small berries on wreath)	

	Good	V. Good	Fine
1853.................................129,694	2.75	3.50	4.75
1854.................................55,358	2.75	3.50	4.75
1855.................................56,500	2.75	3.50	4.75
1856.................................40,430	3.25	3.75	6.00
1857.................................35,180	5.25	6.75	12.50

U. S. LARGE COPPER CENTS

(First coined in 1793; last year of coinage, 1857.)

A very interesting and popular series; more has been written about these coins than any other United States series. They were coined in every year during the period 1793 to 1857 except 1815. There are 60 different die varieties of the cents of 1794 and most of the other dates have a dozen or more. These variations are sometimes slight, often being merely the position of a leaf in the wreath or the spacing of the figures of the date.

In advertisements listing large cents, it is not uncommon to read such notations as, "C. 4C" or "D. 203." These refer to die varieties; "C" denoting Crosby, "D" for Doughty. Various numismatic students have made a study of the varieties of various years and the varieties are named after these students; Crosby for 1793, Chapman for 1794, Doughty for 1795, 1797 to 1814 inclusive, Clapp for 1798, Newcomb 1801, 1802 and 1803, and Newcomb for the years 1816 to 1857 inclusive. However, most collectors are content to acquire just one of each date, and leave the collecting of die varieties to the specialist.

Recommended Reference Books

For those who care to go into the detail study of large cent varieties the following books are recommended:
  "The Cents and Half Cents of 1793" by S. S. Crosby.
  "The Cents of 1794" by Chapman.
  "United States Cents" by Francis W. Doughty.
  "Cents of 1798 and 1799" by Geo. Clapp.
  "Cents of 1801, 1802 and 1803" by Newcomb.
  "United States Copper Cents 1816-1857" by Newcomb.
  "Cents 1795, 1796, 1797 and 1800" by Clapp.
  "Penny Whimsy" by Sheldon, Paschal and Breen.

Condition Is Important

Condition plays a big part in the value of a large cent, especially the early dates. Evidence of this is brought out by a comparison of the lowest grade price with the highest in the premium values following.

Rare Dates Often Faked

In collecting large cents these three dates especially should be purchased from reliable dealers only who will guarantee the genuineness of the coins. The 1793 is frequently "electrotyped." An electrotype can generally be determined by examining the edge to determine if two shells have been placed together. Cents of 1799 will be found "electrotyped" and also made by altering the "8" of the more common 1798 to a "9." An examination of a suspicious piece under a magnifying glass will generally reveal the alteration. Fake cents of 1804 are made by altering most any of the other dates of the same general type, an 1801 being most frequently used. A quick way to check this point is to determine whether the "O" in the date is directly opposite the "O" in OF on the reverse. The peculiarity is found on genuine cents of 1804 and if the piece has been made by altering another date the cipher and the O will not be exactly opposite.

LARGE CENTS

Restrike of the 1804 Cent

A fake 1804 was manufactured in the U. S. Mint by some employees of that institution about the year 1860 to satisfy the demand for this rare date. This piece is known as the "restrike" but fortunately for collectors it was a patchwork job and easily distinguished from a genuine 1804 cent. An old rusty die was used for the obverse which makes the field of the coin pitted and a die of about the year 1818, which is much different from an 1804, was used for the reverse. To aid collectors, an illustration of 1804 restrike is shown here.

Terms Used in Describing Large Cents

Chain Type — The first type of year 1793, has an endless chain of links on the reverse.

Lettered Edge — Some 1793, 1794 and 1795 cents have lettering, "One Hundred for a Dollar" on the edge.

Broken Die — Cracks or lumps on the coin caused by the die breaking or cracking.

Stemless Wreath — See Half Cents.

Wreaths to Stems — See Half Cents.

Crosslet and Plain 4 — See Half Cents.

Over-Date — See Half Cents.

The terms, "wide date," "compact date," "large letters," "small letters," "plain hair-cord," "beaded hair-cord," "large fraction," "small fraction," etc., are also used and are self-explanatory.

The following abbreviations are used in describing large cents:

Let. Ed. — lettered edge; *Lib.* — liberty; *Pl. Ed.* — plain edge; *Ov.* — over; *Perf.* — perfect; *Frac.* — fraction; *Sm.* — small; *Lg.* — large; *Up.* — upright; *Sl.* — slanting.

Fair — Date and devices clear enough to identify.

Good—Lettering worn but readable. Bust has no detail.

Very Good — Date and lettering distinct, some details of head visible.

Fine — About half of hair, etc. details show.

	Quan. Minted	Fair	Good	V. Good	Fine
1793 All kinds	112,212				
Chain, AMERI.		$70.00	$120.00	$180.00	$330.00
Chain, AMERICA		52.50	97.50	157.50	250.00

[23]

LARGE CENTS

Strawberry
Sprig
Variety

	Quan. Minted	Fair	Good	V. Good	Fine
1793 Wreath type (Illustrated above)......101,156		$ 37.50	$ 72.50	$ 97.50	$160.00
Wreath type, strawberry sprig (4 known)....................					
Liberty cap..............11,056		115.00	177.50	290.00	475.00

1794.........................918,521		6.50	16.00	20.00	32.50
(There are many varieties of this date.)					
1795 All kinds.................82,000		5.00	12.50	16.50	24.00
1795 Lettered edge..................		11.00	20.00	30.00	50.00
1796 All kinds................974,700					
Liberty cap....................		8.25	15.00	27.50	38.50

Fair — Clear enough to identify.

Good — Lettering worn, but clear: date clear. Bust lacks details.

Very Good — Drapery partly visible. Less wear in date and lettering.

Fine — Hair over brow is smooth, some detail showing elsewhere.

1796 Draped Bust....................		8.00	15.00	22.50	32.50
1797 All kinds.................897,510		3.00	5.75	9.00	16.50
1797 Stemless.......................		10.00	24.00	42.00	67.00
1798 All kinds.................979,700					
8 over 7......................		6.50	12.00	22.00	40.00
Perfect date..................		2.25	3.75	5.75	10.00
1799 (Beware of altered date)					
All kinds..............904,585					
9 over 8......................		80.00	137.50	220.00	350.00
Perfect date..................		67.50	120.00	175.00	300.00
1800.......................2,822,175		2.25	4.50	6.75	12.00
1801.......................1,362,837		2.25	4.50	6.75	12.00
1802.......................3,435,100		1.50	3.25	5.00	8.00

LARGE CENTS

	Quan. Minted	Fair	Good	V. Good	Fine
1803	2,471,353	$ 1.75	$ 3.75	$ 5.25	$ 9.00
1804	756,838	40.00	67.50	120.00	180.00
So-called "Mint Restrike" (See page 23)				Unc.	40.00
(Obv. altered die of 1803, Rev. of 1818)					
1805	941,116	2.00	3.75	7.00	11.00
1806	348,000	4.25	9.50	17.50	30.00
1807	727,221	2.00	3.75	7.00	11.00

Fair — Details clear enough to identify.

Good — Legends, stars, date worn, but plain.

V. Good—LIBERTY all readable. Ear shows. Details worn but plain.

Fine — Hair on forehead and before ear nearly smooth. Ear and hair under ear sharp.

	Quan. Minted	Fair	Good	V. Good	Fine
1808	1,109,000	2.50	6.50	11.00	17.50
1809	222,867	12.00	27.50	42.50	65.00
1810	1,458,500	2.00	4.75	8.00	11.50
1811	218,025	8.50	12.50	18.00	35.00
1812	1,075,500	1.75	3.75	7.00	8.50
1813	418,000	3.25	8.25	15.00	23.50
1814	357,830	1.50	3.50	5.75	9.00

Good — Head details partly visible. Even wear in date and legends.
V. Good—LIBERTY, date, stars, legends clear. Part of hair cord visible.
Fine — All hairlines show. Hair cords show uniformly.

	Quan. Minted	Good	V. Good	Fine
1816	2,820,982	1.90	2.75	4.75
1817	3,948,400	1.75	2.65	4.50
1818	3,167,000	1.50	2.50	4.00
1819	2,671,000	1.50	2.50	4.00
1820	4,407,550	1.50	2.50	3.50
1821	389,000	6.00	10.00	17.50
1822	2,072,339	2.00	3.00	4.50
1823	855,730	9.50	15.00	23.50
1824	1,262,000	2.00	3.75	5.25
1825	1,461,100	2.00	3.50	5.00
1826	1,517,425	2.00	3.00	4.75
1827	2,357,732	1.50	2.25	3.75
1828	2,260,624	1.75	2.75	4.00
1829	1,414,500	1.50	2.25	3.75
1830	1,711,500	1.50	2.25	3.75

LARGE CENTS

	Quan. Minted	Good	V. Good	Fine
1831	3,359,260	$1.50	$2.25	$3.25
1832	2,362,000	1.65	2.40	3.50
1833	2,739,000	1.50	2.25	3.25
1834	1,855,100	1.75	2.50	4.75
1835	3,878,400	1.50	2.25	4.00
1836	2,111,000	1.50	2.25	4.50
1837	5,558,300	1.25	1.75	3.00
1838	6,370,200	1.25	1.65	2.50
1839 All kinds	3,128,661			
Over 36		40.00	62.50	92.50
Perfect date		2.50	3.50	6.00
1840	2,462,700	2.00	2.60	4.00
1841	1,597,367	2.00	2.60	4.00
1842	2,383,390	2.00	2.60	4.00
1843	2,428,320	2.25	3.00	4.50
1844	2,398,752	1.50	1.85	3.00
1845	3,894,804	1.25	1.75	2.65
1846	4,120,800	1.00	1.25	2.00
1847	6,183,669	1.00	1.25	2.00
1848	6,415,799	1.00	1.25	2.00
1849	4,178,500	1.00	1.25	2.00
1850	4,426,844	1.00	1.25	2.00
1851	9,889,707	1.00	1.25	2.00
1852	5,063,094	1.00	1.25	2.00

1853	6,641,131	1.00	1.25	2.00
1854	4,236,156	1.00	1.25	2.00
1855	1,574,829	1.25	1.75	2.65
1856	2,690,463	1.15	1.50	2.40
1857	333,456	8.50	10.00	14.00

Only a small fraction of the Large Cents issued over a period of 64 years are available. It is an interesting fact that the Treasury Department made a special effort to retire these coins in 1857. They were considered too large for use in business transactions. The smaller coin was considerably more popular. Details of exchange are covered in a circular issued by the mint April 27, 1857.

Following are excerpts from this regulation:

"1. On and after the twenty-fifth day of May next, applications may be made at the mint for cents of the new issue in exchange for . . . the Spanish Pillar Dollar, and the Mexican Dollar . . . or in exchange for the copper cents heretofore issued.

2. The silver or copper coins must be in even sums of five dollars . . . not exceeding fifty dollars. . . ."

This bulletin will help us to understand what has become of a great many large copper cents.

FLYING EAGLE CENTS

Authorized for Circulation in 1857

The first issue of the present small-sized cent. Those of 1856 are generally considered to be patterns but were issued in rather large number for a pattern coin. It is said that there were about 1,000 pieces struck of the commonest variety of the 1856 (copper-nickel or thick planchet, tobacco wreath on reverse). In all there are twelve varieties of the 1856. Cents of the flying eagle type dated 1857 and 1858 are common, except in proof condition; in that condition they are quite expensive. "United States of America" on the flying eagle cent of 1858 comes in two sizes of letters. These types are known as "small letters" and "large letters" (abbreviated, L.L. and S.L.). On the small letter variety the A and M in America are separated; the large letter variety shows these two letters joined at the base.

Fake 1856's are made by altering an 1858. Such species are recognized by the thickness of the lower half of the manufactured "6." (See page 12.)

Good — All details worn, but readable.

V. Good — Feather details and eye of Eagle are evident, but worn.

Fine — Eagle head details and feather tips sharp.

V. Fine — Eagle's eye very bold. Feather ends on right wing worn smooth, considerable detail in right wing and tail.

	Quan. Minted	Good	V. Good	Fine	V. Fine	Unc.	Proof
1856		$375.00	$435.00	$625.00	$725.00	$1400.00	$1750.00
1857	17,450,000	2.00	3.00	5.00	7.75		
1858 All Kinds	24,600,000						
Large Letters		2.85	4.25	6.50	13.00		
Small Letters		2.85	4.25	6.50	13.00		

INDIAN HEAD CENTS

(Coinage for general circulation from 1859 to 1909)

Those of the years 1859 to 1863 were struck in copper-nickel and are commonly termed "white cents" because the metal is of lighter color. In 1864 the metal was changed to the present-used bronze, although copper-nickel cents of 1864 were struck, too. Soon after the change of metal the initial "L," for the engraver Longacre, was placed on the ribbon of the headdress. The "L" variety was struck in smaller quantity than the earlier variety without it, and is therefore quite rare. The "L" appears on the ribbon under the last feather of the headdress on *all* dates to 1909.

Abbreviations peculiar to this series are:

IH. or IND. HD. — Indian Head.

C.-N. — Copper-nickel.

Note: Indian head cents having the date 1858 were not struck for circulation. They are patterns.

INDIAN HEAD CENTS

Good — No LIBERTY visible.

V. Good — At least half of LIBERTY readable.

Fine — LIBERTY completely visible.

V. Fine — Slight but even wear on LIBERTY.

Without shield at top of
wreath on reverse

	Quan. Minted	Good	V. Good	Fine	V. Fine
1859 Indian Head, Cop.-Nic.	36,400,000	$ 1.75	$ 2.65	$4.50	$ 7.75

With shield
on reverse

1860	20,566,000	1.60	2.50	3.75	5.75
1861	10,100,000	4.00	5.25	7.75	10.00
1862	28,075,000	1.00	1.50	2.25	4.00
1863	49,840,000	.95	1.35	2.00	3.00
1864 Cop.-Nic	13,740,000	2.75	4.00	5.50	8.25
1864 Bronze (no L on ribbon)	39,233,714	1.25	2.50	4.75	7.25
1864 Bronze (L on ribbon, must be visible)		9.50	20.00	35.00	50.00
1865	35,429,286	1.00	1.75	3.00	5.00
1866	9,826,500	5.50	8.50	15.00	25.00
1867	9,821,000	5.50	8.50	15.00	25.00
1868	10,266,500	5.50	8.50	15.00	25.00
1869	6,420,000	9.00	15.00	27.50	40.00
1870	5,275,000	7.50	12.50	20.00	30.00
1871	3,929,500	12.50	20.00	27.50	40.00
1872	4,042,000	15.00	25.00	35.00	50.00
1873	11,676,500	2.75	4.00	6.50	10.50
1874	14,187,500	2.75	4.00	7.25	13.00
1875	13,528,000	2.75	4.00	7.25	13.00
1876	7,944,000	3.75	7.25	10.00	15.00
1877	852,500	52.50	72.50	100.00	145.00
1878	5,799,850	4.00	7.50	10.00	15.00
1879	16,231,200	1.00	1.35	2.50	4.00
1880	38,964,955	.55	.90	2.00	3.75
1881	39,211,575	.55	.90	2.00	3.75
1882	38,581,100	.55	.90	2.00	3.75
1883	45,598,109	.45	.80	1.75	3.25
1884	23,261,742	1.25	1.75	3.25	5.50
1885	11,765,384	2.00	4.00	7.50	11.00
1886	17,654,290	1.25	1.75	3.75	6.00

INDIAN HEAD CENTS

	Quan. Minted	Good	V. Good	Fine	V. Fine
1887	45,226,483	$ .25	$ .35	$ .85	$1.80
1888	37,494,414	.25	.35	.85	1.80
1889	48,869,361	.25	.35	.75	1.50
1890	57,182,854	.25	.35	.75	1.50
1891	47,072,350	.25	.35	.75	1.50
1892	37,649,832	.25	.35	1.00	2.00
1893	46,642,195	.25	.35	.75	1.50
1894	16,752,132	.75	1.25	3.25	5.00
1895	38,343,636	.20	.25	.75	1.50
1896	39,057,293	.20	.25	.75	1.50
1897	50,466,330	.20	.25	.65	1.35
1898	49,823,079	.20	.25	.60	1.00
1899	53,600,031	.20	.25	.55	.90
1900	66,833,764	.15	.20	.40	.65
1901	79,611,143	.15	.20	.40	.65
1902	87,376,722	.15	.20	.40	.65
1903	85,094,493	.15	.20	.40	.65
1904	61,328,015	.15	.20	.40	.65
1905	80,719,163	.15	.20	.40	.65
1906	96,022,255	.15	.20	.40	.65
1907	108,138,618	.15	.20	.40	.65
1908	32,327,987	.15	.20	.45	.70
1908S	1,115,000	10.00	12.50	16.00	22.50
1909 Indian	14,370,645	.25	.40	.60	1.00
1909S Indian	309,000	42.50	47.50	60.00	75.00

LINCOLN CENTS

(Coined 1909 to date)

The first year of the Lincoln cent, 1909, comes with and without the small letters "VDB" on the reverse near the lower edge. These letters are the initials of the designer, Victor D. Brenner. There was some protest about the placing of the initials on the coin and they were removed, only to be replaced on the cents of 1918 and thereafter in new position, under Lincoln's bust, in letters so small that an uncirculated piece is often necessary for examination to find it.

Good — Date worn but apparent. Lines in wheatears missing.

V. Good — Lines show in upper wheatears.

Fine — Wheat lines worn but visible.

V. Fine — Cheek, and jaw bones worn but separated. No worn spots on wheatears.

	Quan. Minted	Good	V. Good	Fine	V. Fine
1909 Lincoln Head	72,702,618	.01	.02	.05	.15
1909 V.D.B. (See page 13)	27,995,000	.10	.15	.25	.45
1909S	1,825,000	22.00	24.00	27.50	31.00
1909S V.D.B.	484,000	90.00	110.00	122.50	135.00
1910	146,801,218	.01	.02	.05	.15
1910S	6,045,000	2.00	2.50	3.00	4.00
1911	101,177,787	.01	.02	.05	.15

LINCOLN CENTS

	Quan. Minted	Good	V. Good	Fine	V.Fine
1911D	12,672,000	$ .40	$ .80	$1.60	$3.00
1911S	4,026,000	6.00	7.50	9.00	10.00
1912	68,153,060	.01	.02	.05	.25
1912D	10,411,000	.75	1.00	2.50	4.50
1912S	4,431,000	3.25	4.00	5.00	7.00
1913	76,532,352	.01	.02	.05	.25
1913D	15,804,000	.25	.55	1.75	2.75
1913S	6,101,000	2.25	2.75	3.25	4.50
1914	75,238,432	.05	.30	1.00	1.60
1914D*	1,193,000	31.00	36.00	48.00	70.00
1914S	4,137,000	3.00	4.00	5.00	7.00
1915	29,092,120	.15	.35	1.50	2.25
1915D	22,050,000	.15	.25	.65	1.40
1915S	4,833,000	2.50	3.00	3.50	5.00
1916	131,833,677	.01	.02	.20	.35
1916D	35,956,000	.10	.25	1.25	2.00
1916S	22,510,000	.20	.35	1.25	2.00
1917	196,429,785	.03	.10	.30	.45
1917D	55,120,000	.05	.20	.40	1.25
1917S	32,620,000	.05	.20	.40	1.25
1918	288,104,634	.03	.05	.20	.35
1918D	47,830,000	.10	.25	.50	1.50
1918S	34,680,000	.10	.25	.50	1.50
1919	392,021,000	.05	.08	.15	.40
1919D	57,154,000	.07	.15	.60	1.50
1919S	139,760,000	.07	.15	.60	1.50
1920	310,165,000	.05	.10	.20	.35
1920D	49,280,000	.10	.20	.45	1.25
1920S	46,220,000	.10	.20	.45	1.25
1921	39,157,000	.10	.20	.45	1.50
1921S	15,274,000	.30	.55	1.25	6.00
1922D (All kinds)	7,160,000	2.00	3.00	4.00	5.00
1922 Denver Mint (Without D)					
Beware Alterations		9.00	13.00	20.00	30.00
1923	74,723,000	.03	.07	.15	.30
1923S	8,700,000	.50	1.25	3.00	8.00
1924	75,178,000	.03	.05	.10	.40
1924D	2,520,000	7.50	9.00	12.50	16.50
1924S	11,696,000	.35	.65	1.50	4.00
1925	139,949,000	.03	.05	.10	.20
1925D	22,580,000	.03	.10	.50	1.00
1925S	26,380,000	.10	.25	.75	1.35
1926	157,088,000	.03	.05	.10	.20
1926D	28,020,000	.05	.20	.50	.85
1926S	4,550,000	2.00	3.00	4.00	5.00
1927	144,440,000	.03	.05	.15	.25
1927D	27,170,000	.10	.20	.45	.65
1927S	14,276,000	.15	.30	1.00	1.75
1928	134,116,000	.03	.05	.10	.20
1928D	31,170,000	.10	.20	.35	.75
1928S	17,266,000	.12	.25	.40	1.00
1929	185,262,000	.02	.04	.06	.10
1929D	41,730,000	.03	.07	.10	.15

*Beware of altered date. No VDB on genuine 1914D coin.

LINCOLN CENTS

	Quan. Minted	Good	V. Good	Fine	V. Fine
1929S	50,148,000	$ .03	$ .07	$ .10	$ .15
1930	157,415,000	.01	.03	.05	.08
1930D	40,100,000	.05	.07	.10	.15
1930S	24,286,000	.05	.07	.10	.15
1931	19,396,000	.05	.10	.20	.35
1931D	4,480,000	2.00	2.50	3.75	4.50
1931S	866,000	25.00	30.00	35.00	37.50
1932	9,062,000	.15	.30	.40	.70
1932D	10,500,000	.15	.35	.50	.80
1933	14,360,000	.20	.25	.40	.95
1933D	6,200,000	1.75	2.00	2.75	3.00
1934	219,080,000	.01	.01	.01	.01
1934D	28,446,000	.01	.01	.01	.01
1935	245,388,000	.01	.01	.01	.01
1935D	47,000,000	.01	.01	.01	.01
1935S	38,702,000	.01	.01	.01	.01
Proof quantities shown in parentheses					
1936 (5,569)	309,637,569	.01	.01	.01	.01
1936D	40,620,000	.01	.01	.01	.01
1936S	29,130,000	.01	.01	.01	.01
1937 (9,320)	309,179,320	.01	.01	.01	.01
1937D	50,430,000	.01	.01	.01	.01
1937S	34,500,000	.01	.01	.01	.01
1938 (14,734)	156,696,734	.01	.01	.01	.01
1938D	20,010,000	.01	.01	.01	.01
1938S	15,180,000	.01	.01	.01	.01
1939 (13,520)	316,479,520	.01	.01	.01	.01
1939D	15,160,000	.10	.15	.25	.45
1939S	52,070,000	.01	.01	.01	.01
1940 (15,872)	586,825,872	.01	.01	.01	.01
1940D	81,390,000	.01	.01	.01	.01
1940S	112,940,000	.01	.01	.01	.01
1941 (21,100)	887,039,100	.01	.01	.01	.01
1941D	128,700,000	.01	.01	.01	.01
1941S	92,360,000	.01	.01	.01	.01
1942 (32,600)	657,828,600	.01	.01	.01	.01
1942D	206,698,000	.01	.01	.01	.01
1942S	85,590,000	.01	.01	.01	.01

WARTIME STEEL CENTS

No bronze cents were officially issued in 1943, although a few may have been struck in error. The steel cents of 1943 will be attracted to a magnet while bronze cents will not.

1943	684,628,670	.01	.01	.01	.01
1943D	217,660,000	.01	.01	.01	.01
1943S	191,550,000	.01	.01	.01	.01

"SHELL CASE" COPPER CENTS

1944	1,435,400,000	.01	.01	.01	.01
1944D	430,578,000	.01	.01	.01	.01
1944S	282,760,000	.01	.01	.01	.01
1945	1,040,515,000	.01	.01	.01	.01
1945D	226,268,000	.01	.01	.01	.01
1945S	181,770,000	.01	.01	.01	.01

LINCOLN CENTS
Pre-War Composition — Bronze

	Quan. Minted	V. Fine
1946	991,655,000	$ .01
1946D	315,690,000	.01
1946S	198,100,000	.01
1947	190,555,000	.01
1947D	194,750,000	.01
1947S	99,000,000	.01
1948	317,570,000	.01
1948D	172,637,500	.01
1948S	81,735,000	.01
1949	217,490,000	.01
1949D	154,370,500	.01
1949S	64,290,000	.01
1950 (51,386)	272,686,386	.01
1950D	334,950,000	.01
1950S	118,505,000	.01
1951 (57,500)	294,633,500	.01
1951D	625,355,000	.01
1951S	100,890,000	.01
1952 (81,980)	186,856,980	.01
1952D	746,130,000	.01
1952S	137,800,004	.01
1953 (128,800)	256,883,800	.01
1953D	700,515,000	.01
1953S	181,835,000	.01
1954 (233,300)	71,873,350	.05
1954D	251,552,500	.01
1954S	96,190,000	.01
1955 (378,200)	330,958,200	.01
1955 Double Die Obverse (See picture on page 14)		—
1955D	563,257,500	.01
1955S	44,610,000	.10
1956 (669,384)	421,414,384	.01
1956D	1,098,201,100	.01
1957 (1,247,952)	283,787,952	.01
1957D	1,051,342,000	.01
1958 (875,652)	253,400,652	.01
1958D	800,953,300	.01

Lincoln Memorial Type

		V. Fine
1959 (1,149,291)	610,864,291	.01
1959D	1,279,760,000	.01
1960 Large Date (Proofs All kinds 1,691,602)	588,096,602	.01
1960 Small Date		.50
1960D Large Date	1,580,884,000	.01
1960D Small Date		.01
1961 (3,028,244)	756,373,244	.01
1961D	1,753,266,700	.01

LINCOLN CENTS

	Quan. Minted	V. Fine
1962 (3,218,019)	609,263,019	.01
1962D	1,793,148,400	.01
1963		.01
1963D		.01

"HARD TIMES" AND CIVIL WAR TOKENS

In addition to the coins issued by the United States government, numismatists include in their collection the "Hard Times" and Civil War tokens which circulated as money during two periods in this country's history when nearly all the minor coin was hoarded.

The Hard Times tokens were issued in the period 1834-1844 and are the size of the U.S. cent. They were generally struck in copper in two general groups: political tokens whose theme centered around President Jackson's fight against the United States Bank, and those issued by merchants (tradesman's cards). Common varieties are worth 5¢ to 10¢ each.

During the Civil War small coin was again hoarded; millions of privately coined tokens of political or advertising nature were placed in circulation. Some 10,000 different varieties have been discovered, most of which are more or less common and worth from 5¢ to 10¢ each. A large majority of the Civil War tokens are about the same size as the present day one-cent piece.

All Cents of 1922 Struck at Denver

An explanation of this variety (without mint mark D) was printed in November, 1962, issue of The Numismatic Scrapbook Magazine. Apparently the die from which these coins were struck became filled and the D beneath the date did not appear on several hundred coins that were released for actual circulation.

The number of coins released without the mint mark was very small and therefore they are worth many times the value of those coins with the mint mark showing. ★ ★ ★

The first Lincoln Cents were coined at the Philadelphia Mint June 10, 1909, 420 pieces with V.D.B. struck in matte proof.

★ ★ ★

The first cent to bear the motto "In God We Trust" was the Lincoln Cent.

★ ★ ★

The first cent struck at a branch mint was in 1908, the San Francisco Indian Head Cent.

Beware of altered dates on 1914D Cents. There are no designer's initials VDB on genuine specimens. See details page 13.

★ ★ ★

E Pluribus Unum (One composed of many) is the most familiar legend to be found on U.S. Coins. Its equivalent, but with different wording, appeared on money issued prior to the establishment of the mint. Here are a few: A 1776 New York note, "Uno Eodemque Igne" (One and the same fire). One of the Continental notes pictures a harp with 13 strings accompanied by this motto, "Majora Minoribua Consonant" (The greater and the smaller ones sound together). On another note is a circled chain of 13 links and the motto, "We are one."

One of the most useful purposes of our money has been to constantly remind us of the basis of our national structure.

★ ★ ★

Prices are controlled by supply and demand and are therefore subject to change without notice. Prices offered are for coins in used condition. The same coins in uncirculated or proof condition are worth more.

TWO-CENT BRONZE

(Coined 1864 to 1873)

Those of 1864 are of two varieties: small letters in the motto, "In God We Trust," and the second variety has the same letters in a slightly larger size. Those of the large motto variety are the commonest of the two-cent pieces, while the small motto is the rarest. It is a little difficult to distinguish the two sizes of mottos without some study. The D in GOD is wide in proportion to its height on the small motto variety (see page 13). The two-cent piece was the first United States coin to bear the motto, "In God We Trust."

Good — At least IN GOD visible.

V. Good — WE weakly visible.

Fine — Complete Motto visible. WE weak.

Ex. Fine — WE is bold.

	Quan. Minted	Good	V. Good	Fine	Ex. Fine
1864 All kinds	19,847,500				
Small motto		$20.00	$27.50	$37.50	$57.50
Large motto		1.00	1.25	1.75	3.50
1865	13,640,000	1.00	1.25	1.75	3.50
1866	3,177,000	1.25	1.75	2.75	5.75
1867	2,938,750	1.25	1.75	2.75	5.75
1868	2,803,750	1.25	1.75	2.75	5.75
1869	1,546,500	1.75	2.50	3.75	6.25
1870	861,250	2.25	3.00	5.00	8.50
1871	721,250	2.50	3.50	6.50	12.00
1872	65,000	16.50	19.00	24.00	37.50
					Proof
1873 Proofs only					$250.00

NICKEL THREE-CENT PIECES

(Coined from 1865 to 1889)

This coinage was authorized for the purpose of retiring the 3-cent fractional currency notes. All dates are of the same type. The two rarest dates are 1877 and 1878, both of which were struck in proof only. A variety of 1887 has the date engraved over an "86."

Good — Date and legends complete though worn. III smooth.

V. Good — III is half worn. Rims complete.

Fine — Hair curls well defined.

Ex. Fine — Slight, even wear.

	Quan. Minted	Good	V. Good	Fine	Ex. Fine
1865	11,382,000	$ .90	$1.15	$1.50	$2.25
1866	4,801,000	.90	1.15	1.50	2.25
1867	3,915,000	.90	1.15	1.50	2.25
1868	3,252,000	.90	1.15	1.50	2.25
1869	1,604,000	.90	1.15	1.50	2.25

NICKEL THREE-CENT PIECES

	Quan. Minted	Good	V. Good	Fine	Ex. Fine	Proof
1870	1,335,000	$ .90	$1.15	$1.50	$2.25	
1871	604,000	1.50	1.75	2.75	5.00	
1872	862,000	1.50	1.75	2.75	5.00	
1873	1,173,000	.90	1.15	1.50	2.25	
1874	790,000	1.25	1.50	2.50	6.00	
1875	228,000	2.25	2.75	4.00	10.00	
1876	162,000	2.50	3.00	4.00	10.00	
1877 Proofs only						$250.00
1878 Proofs only	2,350					80.00
1879	41,200	1.75	2.50	3.50	6.00	27.50
1880	24,955	2.50	4.00	5.00	7.50	27.50
1881	1,080,575	1.00	1.15	1.50	3.00	22.50
1882	25,300	1.75	2.50	3.50	6.00	27.50
1883	10,609	1.75	2.50	3.50	6.00	27.50
1884	5,642	3.00	4.00	5.00	8.00	20.00
1885	4,790	3.00	4.00	5.00	8.00	20.00
1886 Proofs only	4,290					20.00
1887 87 over 86 (Proofs only)						85.00
1887	7,961	6.00	8.50	11.00	18.00	70.00
1888	41,083	2.00	2.50	3.50	6.50	16.00
1889	21,561	2.00	2.50	3.50	6.50	16.00

FIVE-CENT NICKELS

(Coined from 1866 to date)

Authorized for the purpose of retiring fractional currency notes of the denomination of less than 10 cents.

The first type is known as the "shield type" and has two varieties; both 1866 and 1867 have rays through the stars (1867 also was coined without the rays). Proofs only were coined for the years 1877 and 1878, the former being the rarest date of the shield type and also of the entire 5-cent nickel series, except 1913.

In 1883 the type was changed to the more or less familiar "liberty head." This type first appeared without the word "cents" on the coin; merely a large letter "V" to denote denomination. As this coin is about the size of a five-dollar gold piece these "cent-less" nickels were immediately gold-plated and passed on unsuspecting people for five dollars. Later in the year the word "cents" was added. The cent-less variety was hoarded in great numbers and frequently turns up today. 1885 and 1912S mint are the rarest dates of this type.

The 1913 Liberty Head Nickel did not become known to the numismatic world until 1920, when five specimens were exhibited at a meeting of coin collectors in Chicago. Very clever fake 1913's have been made by altering 1903 and 1910 nickels.

Indian Head type nickels were first coined in 1913 with the buffalo or "bison" standing on "raised" ground. This is known as Variety 1; the ground or plane was recessed to form Variety 2.

In 1938 the Treasury of the United States announced a public competition for a new design, it being specified that the head of Jefferson and a reproduction of his home, Monticello, be the important features. Some 390 entries were received and Felix Schlag of Chicago won the $1,000 prize.

FIVE-CENT NICKELS

Rays   Without Rays

Good — All letters in Motto readable.
V. Good — Motto stands out clearly. Rims worn slightly but even. Part of shield lines visible.
Fine — Half of each olive leaf is smooth.
Ex. Fine — Leaf tips show slight wear. Cross over shield slightly worn.

	Quan. Minted	Good	V. Good	Fine	Ex. Fine
1866 Rays through stars	14,742,500	$2.25	$2.75	$4.50	$12.00
1867 All kinds	30,909,500				
Rays		3.25	4.75	10.50	23.00
1867 Without Rays		.90	1.25	1.50	3.25
1868	28,817,000	.90	1.10	1.60	4.00
1869	16,395,000	1.25	1.50	2.50	4.50
1870	4,806,000	2.00	2.25	3.50	6.50
1871	561,000	17.50	20.00	32.50	45.00
1872	6,036,000	2.25	2.75	3.75	7.50
1873	4,550,000	1.25	1.75	3.25	5.50
1874	3,538,000	3.50	4.50	5.50	10.00
1875	2,097,000	6.50	7.50	11.50	26.50
1876	2,530,000	2.75	3.50	5.00	9.00
1877 Proofs only	Est. 500 issued			Proof	500.00
1878 Proofs only	2,350			Proof	110.00
1879	29,100	6.00	7.50	9.00	13.50
1880	19,955	8.00	9.50	12.50	16.50
1881	72,375	5.50	6.50	8.50	13.50
1882	11,476,600	1.00	1.25	2.25	3.50
1883 Shield type	1,456,919	1.50	2.25	3.50	5.00

Without CENTS   With CENTS

Good — No detail in head. LIBERTY obliterated.
V. Good — At least 3 letters in LIBERTY readable.
Fine — All letters in LIBERTY show.
Ex. Fine — LIBERTY sharp. Corn grains at bottom of wreath show, on reverse.

FIVE-CENT NICKELS

	Quan. Minted	Good	V. Good	Fine	Ex. Fine
1883 Liberty, without CENTS.	5,479,519	$ .20	$ .30	$ .75	$1.25
1883 Liberty, with CENTS...	16,032,983	1.35	2.00	4.25	6.00
1884	11,273,942	1.50	2.50	5.00	8.25
1885	1,476,490	30.00	37.50	57.50	72.50
1886	3,330,290	14.00	17.50	24.00	32.50
1887	15,263,652	1.00	1.25	2.50	5.00
1888	10,720,483	2.25	3.00	5.00	9.00
1889	15,881,361	1.00	1.25	2.75	4.50
1890	16,259,272	1.00	1.75	3.00	6.50
1891	16,834,350	1.00	1.25	2.25	4.25
1892	11,699,642	1.00	1.25	2.75	4.50
1893	13,370,195	1.00	1.25	2.00	4.00
1894	5,413,132	2.00	2.50	5.25	9.00
1895	9,979,884	1.00	1.25	2.25	4.50
1896	8,842,920	1.00	1.35	4.00	9.00
1897	20,428,735	.35	.50	1.25	3.50
1898	12,532,087	.30	.40	1.50	3.50
1899	26,029,031	.35	.50	1.50	4.00
1900	27,255,995	.20	.30	1.00	2.50
1901	26,480,213	.15	.25	.75	2.25
1902	31,480,579	.15	.25	.75	2.25
1903	28,006,725	.15	.25	.75	2.25
1904	21,404,984	.15	.25	.75	2.25
1905	29,827,276	.15	.25	.75	2.25
1906	38,613,725	.15	.25	.75	2.25
1907	39,214,800	.15	.25	.75	2.25
1908	22,686,177	.15	.25	.75	2.25
1909	11,590,526	.15	.25	.75	2.25
1910	30,169,353	.15	.25	.75	2.25
1911	39,559,372	.15	.25	.75	2.25
1912	26,236,714	.15	.25	.75	2.25
1912D	8,474,000	.50	1.25	3.50	14.00
1912S	238,000	12.50	16.00	22.50	50.00

1913 Liberty Head (not a regular issue, beware altered date).

James E. Fraser, who designed the Buffalo Nickel, used three different Indians to obtain the portrait on the obverse side. These were Irontail, Two Moons, a Cheyenne chief, and another not identified. The bison was modeled after "Black Diamond" in the New York Zoological Garden. The famous animal was slaughtered in 1915 and his massive head was preserved and mounted.

Variety 1   Variety 2

Good — Legends and date readable. Horn worn off.

V. Good — Half horn shows.

Fine — Two-thirds horn shows. Obv. rim intact.

Ex. Fine — Full horn. Slight wear on Indian's hair ribbon.

FIVE-CENT NICKELS

	Quan. Minted	Good	V. Good	Fine	Ex. Fine
1913 Indian head — Variety 1 —					
Bison on mound........30,993,520	$ .20	$ .35	$ .50	$ 1.10
1913D Variety 1 —					
Bison on mound.........5,337,000	.50	1.00	1.50	2.75
1913S Variety 1 —					
Bison on mound........2,105,000	1.50	2.25	3.00	6.50
1913 Indian head — Variety 2 —					
Bison on plane.........29,858,700	.25	.35	.55	1.50
1913D Variety 2 —					
Bison on plane........4,156,000	6.00	8.00	12.00	20.00
1913S Variety 2 —					
Bison on plane........1,209,000	13.50	17.50	22.50	40.00
1914.....................20,665,738	.25	.40	.75	1.75
1914D....................3,912,000	5.00	7.00	12.00	18.00
1914S....................3,470,000	.60	1.50	4.25	11.00
1915.....................20,987,270	.25	.40	.75	2.00
1915D....................7,569,500	.75	1.75	3.75	10.00
1915S....................1,505,000	3.00	4.00	7.00	18.50
1916.....................63,498,066	.05	.20	.50	2.00
1916D....................13,333,000	.50	.90	2.00	7.00
1916S....................11,860,000	.50	1.25	2.50	8.50
1917.....................51,424,029	.05	.10	.25	1.50
1917D....................9,910,800	1.00	1.35	3.75	13.50
1917S....................4,193,000	1.00	1.35	3.75	13.50
1918.....................32,086,314	.05	.20	.50	2.00
1918D All kinds............8,362,000				
8 over 7.....................	50.00	95.00	190.00	525.00
Perfect date.................	.90	1.50	4.25	17.50
1918S....................4,882,000	.90	1.60	4.50	20.00
1919.....................60,868,000	.05	.10	.30	1.00
1919D....................8,006,000	1.25	1.75	4.50	27.50
1919S....................7,521,000	1.25	2.25	5.00	27.50
1920.....................63,093,000	.05	.10	.30	1.00
1920D....................9,418,000	.65	1.25	3.00	22.50
1920S....................9,689,000	.65	1.25	3.00	22.50
1921.....................10,663,000	.05	.20	.40	2.00
1921S....................1,557,000	4.00	6.00	10.00	35.00
1923.....................35,715,000	.05	.10	.30	1.00
1923S....................6,142,000	.60	1.25	2.50	18.00
1924.....................21,620,000	.05	.10	.30	1.00
1924D....................5,258,000	.60	1.00	2.25	17.50
1924S....................1,437,000	1.50	2.50	6.00	35.00
1925.....................35,565,100	.05	.10	.30	1.00
1925D....................4,450,000	1.50	3.00	5.50	16.50
1925S....................6,256,000	1.25	2.50	5.00	17.50
1926.....................44,693,000	.05	.05	.05	.75
1926D....................5,638,000	.50	1.25	1.75	12.50
1926S......................970,000	1.50	2.75	7.00	55.00
1927.....................37,981,000	.05	.05	.05	.75
1927D....................5,730,000	.20	.50	1.00	3.50
1927S....................3,430,000	1.00	2.25	4.50	25.00
1928.....................23,411,000	.05	.05	.05	.45
1928D....................6,436,000	.05	.05	.05	.75
1928S....................6,936,000	.05	.05	.05	3.00

FIVE-CENT NICKELS

	Quan. Minted	Good	V. Good	Fine	Ex. Fine
1929	36,446,000	$ .05	$ .05	$ .05	$ .35
1929D	8,370,000	.05	.05	.05	.50
1929S	7,754,000	.05	.05	.05	.60
1930	22,849,000	.05	.05	.05	.40
1930S	5,435,000	.05	.05	1.25	3.00
1931S	1,200,000	.75	1.75	2.50	5.25
1934	20,213,003	.05	.05	.05	.05
1934D	7,480,000	.05	.05	.05	.05
1935	58,264,000	.05	.05	.05	.05
1935D	12,092,000	.05	.05	.05	.05
1935S	10,300,000	.05	.05	.05	.05
1936 (Proofs 4,420)	119,001,420	.05	.05	.05	.05
1936D	24,418,000	.05	.05	.05	.05
1936S	14,930,000	.05	.05	.05	.05
1937 (Proofs 5,769)	79,485,769	.05	.05	.05	.05
1937D All kinds	17,826,000	.05	.05	.05	.05
1937D* (Three-legged Buffalo)		12.50	14.50	19.00	35.00
1937S	5,635,000	.07	.10	.12	.15
1938D Buffalo — All kinds	7,020,000	.05	.05	.05	.05
1938D over S (See illustration page 14).				3.00	5.00

*Beware of alterations. (Removed leg.)

V. Good — Considerable wear.

Ex. Fine — Cheekbones slightly worn. Hairlines worn but defined. Eyebrows sharp, slightly worn.

	Quan. Minted	Very Good	Ex. Fine		Quan. Minted	Very Good	Ex. Fine
1938 (Proofs 19,365)				1940D	43,540,000	$ .05	$ .05
Jefferson	19,515,365	$ .05	$ .05	1940S	39,690,000	.05	.05
1938D	5,376,000	.25	.75	1941 (Proofs 18,720)			
1938S	4,105,000	.65	1.30		203,283,720	.05	.05
1939 (Proofs 12,535)				1941D	53,432,000	.05	.05
	120,627,535	.05	.05	1941S	43,445,000	.05	.05
1939D	3,514,000	1.00	4.50	1942 (Proofs 29,600)			
1939S	6,630,000	.35	2.00		49,818,600	.05	.05
1940 (Proofs 14,158)				1942D	13,938,000	.10	1.25
	176,499,158	.05	.05				

WARTIME SILVER FIVE-CENT PIECES

(Mint mark above dome on reverse side)

Nickels prior 1956 command a premium if in bright uncirculated condition.

	Quan. Minted	Ex. Fine		Quan. Minted	Ex. Fine
1942P (Proofs 27,600)			1944P	119,150,000	$ .15
	57,900,600	$ .25	1944D	32,309,000	.15
1942S	32,900,000	.15	1944S	21,640,000	.15
1943P	271,165,000	.15	1945P	119,408,100	.10
1943D	15,294,000	.15	1945D	37,158,000	.10
1943S	104,060,000	.15	1945S	58,939,000	.10

FIVE-CENT NICKELS

Pre-War Composition, 75% Copper — 25% Nickel Alloy

	Quan. Minted	Ex. Fine		Quan. Minted	Ex. Fine
1946	161,116,000	$ .05	1953S	19,210,900	$ .05
1946D	45,292,200	.05	1954 (233,300)	47,917,350	.05
1946S	13,560,000	.05	1954D	117,183,060	.05
1947	95,000,000	.05	1954S	29,384,000	.20
1947D	37,882,000	.05	1955 (378,200)	8,266,200	.15
1947S	24,720,000	.05	1955D	74,464,100	.05
1948	89,348,000	.05	1956 (669,384)	35,885,384	.05
1948D	44,734,000	.05	1956D	67,222,940	.05
1948S	11,300,000	.05	1957 (1,247,952)	39,655,952	.05
1949	60,652,000	.05	1957D	136,828,900	.05
1949D	35,238,000	.05	1958 (875,652)	17,963,652	.10
1949S	9,716,000	.05	1958D	168,249,120	.05
1950 (51,386)	9,847,386	.05	1959 (1,149,291)	28,397,291	.05
1950D	2,630,030	7.50	1959D	160,738,240	.05
1951 (57,500)	28,689,500	.05	1960 (1,691,602)	57,107,602	.05
1951D	20,460,000	.05	1960D	192,582,180	.05
1951S	7,776,000	.40	1961 (3,028,244)	76,668,244	.05
1952 (81,980)	64,069,980	.05	1961D	229,342,760	.05
1952D	30,638,000	.05	1962 (3,218,019)	100,602,019	.05
1952S	20,572,000	.05	1962D	280,195,720	.05
1953 (128,800)	46,772,800	.05	1963		.05
1953D	59,878,600	.05	1963D		.05

SILVER THREE-CENT PIECES

(Coined from 1851 to 1873)

Authorized to facilitate postal transactions; however, due to its small size it became unpopular.

The same general design was used throughout the entire coinage except for some minor changes in design and alloy. In 1854 the size of the star on the obverse was enlarged as was the size of the date, and arrows and branches were added. In 1859 the outlines on the star were reduced from three to two and the size of the date was reduced. Those bearing the date 1864 are the rarest of the series.

Good — *Star worn smooth. Legend and date readable.*

V. Good — *Outline of shield defined. Legend and date clear.*

Fine — *Only star points worn smooth.*

V. Fine — *Only partial wear on star ridges.*

SILVER THREE-CENT PIECES

	Quan. Minted	Good	V. Good	Fine	V. Fine
1851	5,447,400	$1.50	$2.75	$3.25	$5.25
1851O	720,000	5.00	10.00	15.00	23.50
1852	18,663,500	1.25	1.75	2.75	4.25
1853	11,400,000	1.25	1.75	2.75	4.25
Three outlines to star, Large Date					
1854	671,000	3.00	3.75	5.75	8.50
1855	139,000	6.00	9.00	14.00	23.00
1856	1,458,000	2.75	3.50	5.00	8.50
1857	1,042,000	2.75	3.50	5.00	8.50
1858	1,604,000	2.50	3.25	4.75	7.50
Two outlines to star, Small Date					
1859	365,000	2.50	3.00	4.00	6.00
1860	287,000	2.50	3.00	4.00	6.00
1861	498,000	1.75	2.75	3.75	5.75
1862	363,550	1.75	2.75	3.75	5.75

	Quan. Minted	Proof
1863	21,460	$ 90.00
1864 Proofs only	470	110.00
1865	8,500	85.00
1866	22,725	35.00
1867	4,625	36.50
1868	4,100	38.50
1869	5,100	38.50
1870	4,000	35.00
1871	4,260	35.00
1872	1,950	35.00
1873 Proofs only	600	75.00

HALF DIMES
(Coined from 1794 to 1873)

Coinage for general circulation started with 1794 although some believe the 1792 half disme to be a regular issue (see page 5). All the early dates, those before 1829, are more or less rare, with the 1802 being one of the great United States silver rarities.

Die varieties are numerous in this series; one curious variety is that of the year 1800 where the word "Liberty" is spelled "LIBEKTY."

Abbreviations used in describing half dimes (those not previously explained in preceding pages) are:

Ars. — arrows. (Arrows at the date on 1853, 1854 and 1855.)
Drap. — drapery. (Drapery on the left elbow of Liberty.)

Fair — *Details clear enough to identify.*
Good — *Eagle, wreath, bust outlined but lack details.*
V. Good — *Some details remain on face. All lettering readable.*

Fine — *Hair ends show. Hair at top smooth.*
V. Fine — *Hairlines at top show. Hair about ear defined.*

	Quan. Minted	Fair	Good	V. Good	Fine	V. Fine
1792 Half Disme		150.00	210.00	275.00	360.00	600.00

HALF DIMES

 1794   1796

	Quan. Minted	Fair	Good	V. Good	Fine	V. Fine
1794................	} 86,416	$ 40.00	$ 80.00	$125.00	$175.00	$325.00
1795................		30.00	52.50	77.50	110.00	200.00
1796................10,230		32.50	67.50	100.00	150.00	220.00
1797 All kinds..........44,527						
15 stars................		20.00	50.00	70.00	120.00	170.00
16 stars................		20.00	50.00	70.00	120.00	170.00
13 stars................		22.50	52.50	75.00	130.00	185.00

1796-1805

Fair — Details clear enough to identify.

Good — Date, stars, LIBERTY readable. Bust outlined but no details.

V. Good — Some details show.

Fine — Hair and drapery lines worn, but visible.

V. Fine — Only left of drapery indistinct.

	Fair	Good	V. Good	Fine	V. Fine
1800 All kinds..........24,000					
Perfect die..............	20.00	35.00	62.50	77.50	150.00
LIBEKTY variety......	25.00	40.00	65.00	82.50	160.00
1801.................33,910	27.50	50.00	85.00	110.00	275.00
1802 (Rare)...........13,010	185.00	375.00	600.00	900.00	1700.00
1803.................37,850	18.50	35.00	57.50	90.00	175.00
1805.................15,600	30.00	60.00	90.00	140.00	260.00

Good — Bust outlined, no detail. Date and legend readable.

V. Good — Complete legend and date plain. At least 3 letters of LIBERTY show clearly.

Fine — All letters in LIBERTY show.

V. Fine — Full rim, both sides. Clasp on shoulder and ear well defined.

	Quan. Minted	Good	V. Good	Fine	V. Fine
1829......................1,230,000		1.75	2.25	3.00	5.00
1830......................1,240,000		1.50	2.00	2.85	5.00
1831......................1,242,700		1.50	2.00	2.85	5.00
1832........................965,000		1.50	2.00	2.85	5.00
1833......................1,370,000		1.50	2.00	2.85	5.00
1834......................1,480,000		1.50	2.00	2.85	5.00
1835......................2,760,000		1.50	2.00	2.85	5.00
1836......................1,900,000		1.50	2.00	2.85	5.00
1837......................2,276,000		1.50	2.00	2.85	5.00

HALF DIMES

Good—*LIBERTY on shield smooth. Date and letters readable.*

V. Good — At least 3 letters in LIBERTY are visible.

Fine — Entire LIBERTY visible, weak spots.

V. Fine — Entire LIBERTY strong and even.

	Quan. Minted	Good	V. Good	Fine	V. Fine
1837 No Stars		$12.00	$16.00	$25.00	$37.50
1838O No Stars		15.00	23.50	35.00	75.00

1838 With stars	2,255,000	1.25	1.75	2.75	5.00
1839	1,069,150	1.10	1.60	2.50	4.50
1839O	1,096,550	2.25	2.50	4.75	8.75
1840	1,344,085	1.10	1.60	2.50	4.00
1840O	935,000	2.25	3.40	6.25	12.25
1841	1,150,000	1.00	1.40	2.40	4.00
1841O	815,000	1.50	2.40	4.25	6.75
1842	815,000	1.00	1.40	2.25	3.65
1842O	350,000	2.10	3.75	7.25	13.75
1843	1,165,000	1.00	1.35	2.10	3.50
1844	430,000	1.50	2.40	4.25	6.00
1844O	220,000	2.90	5.00	9.75	18.25
1845	1,564,000	1.00	1.35	2.10	3.50
1846	27,000	18.00	23.00	36.00	48.00
1847	1,274,000	1.00	1.35	2.10	3.50
1848	668,000	.90	1.35	2.25	3.65
1848O	600,000	2.10	3.40	6.25	12.25
1849	1,309,000	.90	1.25	2.10	3.75
1849O	140,000	12.50	19.00	33.00	45.00
1850	955,000	.90	1.25	2.10	3.50
1850O	690,000	1.50	2.25	4.00	9.50
1851	781,000	.90	1.75	2.00	3.25
1851O	860,000	1.40	2.10	3.75	8.75
1852	1,000,500	.90	1.25	2.10	3.50
1852O	260,000	2.40	4.00	7.25	16.00
1853 With Arrows..All kinds	13,345,020	1.10	1.40	2.00	3.75
No arrows		4.00	6.00	9.75	14.50
1853O With Arrows. All kinds	2,360,000	1.00	1.40	2.00	3.75
No arrows		32.00	40.00	60.00	82.50

Arrows at either side of date were added to indicate reduction of weight. Genuine specimens without arrows should weigh more than specimens with arrows.

HALF DIMES

	Quan. Minted	Good	V. Good	Fine	V. Fine
1854 Arrows	5,740,000	$ .80	$1.00	$ 1.40	$ 3.00
1854O Arrows	1,560,000	1.00	1.40	2.00	4.00
1855 Arrows	1,750,000	.75	1.00	1.40	3.10
1855O Arrows	600,000	1.50	2.40	3.75	8.00
1856 No arrows	4,880,000	.50	.70	1.10	2.25
1856O	1,100,000	1.00	1.40	2.25	4.00
1857	7,280,000	.50	.70	1.10	2.25
1857O	1,380,000	.90	1.25	2.00	3.65
1858	3,500,000	.45	.65	1.10	2.25
1858O	1,660,000	.80	1.20	2.00	3.75
1859	340,000	1.15	1.65	2.75	4.25
1859O	560,000	1.00	1.50	2.50	4.00

In the years 1859 and 1860 a half-dime type was struck which does not bear our nation's identity. These coins are known as transitional patterns, and were struck at the time the inscription UNITED STATES OF AMERICA was being transferred from the reverse to the obverse side of the coin. These coins are not a regular mint issue.

1859 (Obv. of 1859. Rev. of 1860)	Proof	$800.00
1860 Stars		
(Obv. of 1859. Rev. of 1860)...100	Unc.	385.00

	Quan. Minted	Good	V. Good	Fine	V. Fine
1860 Legend	799,000	.75	1.15	2.00	2.75
1860O Legend	1,060,000	1.40	1.85	2.75	4.50
1861	3,281,000	.75	1.00	1.65	2.65
1862	1,492,550	.75	1.00	1.65	2.65
1863	18,460	4.75	5.75	9.50	13.25
1863S	100,000	4.50	6.25	10.00	16.00
1864 (Proofs only)	470			Proof	110.00
1864S	90,000	5.25	8.00	13.75	23.00
1865	13,500	4.50	5.75	8.50	13.75
1865S	120,000	3.65	5.25	8.50	15.00
1866	10,725	2.50	3.00	5.50	10.25
1866S	120,000	2.75	3.00	5.50	11.25
1867	8,625	2.50	3.00	5.50	10.25
1867S	120,000	2.35	3.00	5.00	12.00
1868	85,900	1.25	1.70	2.75	4.65
1868S	280,000	1.10	1.65	2.65	4.50
1869	208,600	1.00	1.35	2.00	2.75
1869S	230,000	1.00	1.40	2.10	4.25
1870	536,600	.75	.95	1.50	2.75
1871	1,488,860	.75	.95	1.50	2.65
1871S	161,000	5.00	7.25	11.50	18.50
1872	2,947,950	.75	1.05	1.75	3.00
1872S Mint Mark below wreath.					
All kinds	837,000	1.00	1.40	2.25	3.65
Mint Mark within wreath		.75	1.15	2.00	3.25
1873	712,600	.65	.85	1.50	2.75
1873S	324,000	.90	1.50	2.75	4.65

DIMES

(Coined from 1796 to date)

The designs of the dimes follow very closely those of the half dime up through the liberty seated type. Also, in similar fashion to half dime, there is nothing

in the design of the early dates to indicate the value of the piece. The early dates are scarce, especially in choice condition.

The liberty head type issued from 1892 to 1916 is erroneously called "Morgan Type." The design was by Barber, and each coin has his initial B on the truncation of the neck.

Fair — Details clear enough to identify.
Good — Date readable. Bust outlined, but no detail.
V. Good — All but deepest drapery folds worn smooth. All hairlines, but curls lack detail.
Fine — All drapery lines visible. Hair partly worn.
V. Fine — Only left side of drapery is indistinct.

	Quan. Minted	Fair	Good	V. Good	Fine	V. Fine
1796	22,135	$75.00	$150.00	$225.00	$350.00	$500.00
1797 All kinds	25,261					
16 stars		55.00	125.00	175.00	325.00	450.00
13 stars		45.00	100.00	150.00	240.00	350.00

1798 All kinds	27,550					
8 over 7, 16 stars on Rev.		25.00	50.00	70.00	95.00	150.00
8 over 7, 13 stars on Rev.		—	—	—	—	—
Perfect date		25.00	50.00	70.00	95.00	150.00
1800	21,760	22.00	47.50	65.00	80.00	135.00
1801	34,640	30.00	60.00	80.00	120.00	185.00
1802	10,975	32.50	57.50	70.00	85.00	145.00
1803	33,040	25.00	52.50	67.50	80.00	135.00
1804	8,265	42.00	75.00	95.00	150.00	290.00
1805	120,780	15.00	30.00	45.00	65.00	95.00
1807	165,000	12.50	27.50	45.00	65.00	95.00

Good — Date, letters and stars discernible. Bust outlined, no details.
V. Good — Legends and date plain. Minimum of 3 letters in LIBERTY show.
Fine — Full LIBERTY. Ear and shoulder clasp visible. Part of rim shows on both sides.
V. Fine—LIBERTY distinct. Full rim. Ear and clasp plain and distinct.

DIMES

	Quan. Minted	Good	V. Good	Fine	V. Fine
1809	44,710	$19.00	$26.00	$39.00	$62.50
1811 11 over 09	65,180	11.00	15.00	24.00	37.50
1814	421,500	4.00	5.75	10.00	16.50
1820	942,587	2.50	3.50	5.75	10.75
1821	1,186,512	2.25	3.25	5.40	10.75
1822	100,000	16.50	19.00	42.50	90.00
1823	440,000	3.25	5.25	10.00	18.00
1824 4 over 2		4.65	6.50	12.00	22.50
1825	510,000	3.25	4.25	6.25	12.00
1827	1,215,000	3.10	3.75	5.50	11.50
1828 All kinds	125,000				
Large Date		8.25	13.00	24.00	33.00
Small Date		4.65	6.00	11.00	19.00

	Quan. Minted	Good	V. Good	Fine	V. Fine
1829 All kinds	770,000	1.30	2.00	3.00	5.50
Large 10c		4.10	5.75	10.00	15.00
1830	510,000	1.15	1.50	2.50	4.75
1831	771,350	1.15	1.50	2.50	4.75
1832	522,500	1.15	1.50	2.50	4.75
1833	485,000	1.30	1.50	2.50	4.85
1834	635,000	1.15	1.50	2.40	4.70
1835	1,410,000	1.15	1.50	2.40	4.70
1836	1,190,000	1.15	1.50	2.40	4.50
1837 All kinds	1,042,000	1.45	2.00	3.00	6.00

Good—LIBERTY on shield smooth. Date and letters readable.

V. Good—At least 3 letters in LIBERTY are visible.

Fine — Entire LIBERTY visible, weak spots.

V. Fine — Entire LIBERTY strong and even.

		Good	V. Good	Fine	V. Fine
1837 Liberty seated, no stars		15.00	22.50	37.50	50.00
1838O Liberty seated, no stars	402,434	20.00	32.50	50.00	85.00

	Quan. Minted	Good	V. Good	Fine	V. Fine
1838	1,992,500	2.00	2.50	3.25	5.85
1839	1,053,115	1.40	1.85	2.75	5.25
1839O	1,243,272	2.00	3.15	5.00	8.00
1840	1,358,580	1.40	2.00	3.00	5.50

DIMES

	Quan. Minted	Good	V. Good	Fine	V. Fine
1840O No drapery	1,175,000	$2.00	$ 2.75	$ 4.00	$ 6.75
1841 Drapery	1,622,500	1.00	1.40	2.00	4.25
1841 No Drapery					
1841O	2,007,500	1.00	1.75	3.00	6.50
1842	1,887,500	1.00	1.40	2.00	4.50
1842O	2,020,000	2.00	2.75	3.75	8.50
1843	1,370,000	1.00	1.40	2.00	4.25
1843O	150,000	6.25	9.00	15.00	27.50
1844	72,500	9.00	15.00	25.00	45.00
1845	1,755,000	1.00	1.40	2.00	4.25
1845O	230,000	3.25	4.50	6.25	12.50
1846	31,300	5.50	7.75	11.25	19.50
1847	245,000	2.00	2.75	4.00	8.25
1848	451,500	1.50	2.25	2.75	5.65
1849	839,000	1.00	1.40	2.00	4.50
1849O	300,000	2.75	3.75	5.50	12.75
1850	1,931,500	1.00	1.40	2.00	3.75
1850O	510,000	2.40	3.50	5.50	11.00
1851	1,026,500	1.00	1.40	2.00	4.00
1851O	400,000	2.00	2.65	3.75	8.25
1852	1,535,500	1.00	1.40	2.00	4.00
1852O	430,000	2.00	3.00	4.50	10.00
1853 All kinds	12,173,010				
No arrows at date		5.75	7.50	10.50	19.00
With arrows		1.10	1.60	2.25	4.75
1853O (Arrows)	1,100,000	2.00	3.50	3.40	5.75
1854 (Arrows)	4,470,000	1.00	1.40	2.00	3.75
1854O (Arrows)	1,770,000	1.10	1.65	2.50	5.25
1855 (Arrows)	2,075,000	.70	1.00	1.50	3.00
1856	5,780,000	.75	1.05	1.50	3.25
1856O	1,180,000	1.40	1.85	2.50	4.25
1856S	70,000	12.50	17.50	25.00	55.00
1857	5,580,000	.90	1.35	1.40	3.00
1857O	1,540,000	1.10	1.60	2.25	4.50
1858	1,540,000	.65	1.10	2.00	3.00
1858O	290,000	2.00	2.75	4.00	7.50
1858S	60,000	7.75	11.00	15.00	37.50
1859	430,000	.65	1.05	1.75	4.25
1859 Obv. of 1859. Rev. of 1860					
1859O	480,000	.75	1.20	2.00	4.75
1859S	60,000	7.00	9.50	12.50	25.00
1860S (Stars on Obv.)	140,000	3 75	6.00	9.50	19.00

1860 (Legend replaces stars)	607,000	.90	1.35	1.90	3.50
1860O (Rare)	40,000	32.50	50.00	70.00	125.00
1861	1,924,000	.50	.90	1.15	2.25
1861S	172,500	5.50	8.50	14.00	25.00
1862	847,550	1.10	1.45	2.00	3.75

DIMES

	Quan. Minted	Good	V. Good	Fine	V. Fine
1862S	180,750	$ 3.75	$ 6.25	$ 10.00	$ 20.00
1863	14,460	3.75	5.00	7.00	10.00
1863S	157,500	3.75	6.25	10.00	21.00
1864	39,070	3.75	5.50	7.50	10.50
1864S	230,000	4.00	6.50	10.50	17.50
1865	10,500	3.75	4.75	6.25	9.75
1865S	175,000	4.25	6.50	10.00	13.00
1866	8,725	3.50	4.50	6.25	10.00
1866S	135,000	3.75	5.75	8.75	15.75
1867	6,625	3.75	5.25	7.50	10.75
1867S	140,000	3.65	5.75	8.50	14.00
1868	466,250	.90	1.40	1.65	3.10
1868S	260,000	2.75	4.00	6.00	10.25
1869	256,600	1.00	1.40	2.00	3.75
1869S	450,000	2.75	3.90	5.75	12.75
1870	471,500	.90	1.50	2.50	4.00
1870S	50,000	20.00	27.50	40.00	57.50
1871	753,610	.90	1.35	2.00	3.50
1871CC	20,100	65.00	92.50	132.50	250.00
1871S	320,000	4.25	5.65	9.50	18.50
1872	2,396,450	.75	1.25	2.00	3.25
1872CC	24,000	45.00	60.00	87.50	175.00
1872S	190,000	4.50	6.25	8.75	14.75
1873 No Arrows	1,568,600	.75	3.25	5.50	4.00
1873 With Arrows	2,378,500	4.50	6.00	8.50	16.00
1873CC No Arrows (unique)	12,400				
1873CC With Arrows	18,791	200.00	300.00	425.00	500.00
1873S With Arrows	455,000	7.00	10.00	15.00	22.50
1874 With Arrows	2,940,700	4.50	6.00	8.50	16.00
1874CC With Arrows	10,817	47.50	72.50	120.00	190.00
1874S With Arrows	240,000	7.00	10.00	15.00	24.00
1875	10,350,700	.50	.85	1.25	2.50
1875CC	4,645,000	.75	1.10	1.75	3.75
1875S	9,070,000	.75	1.05	1.50	3.00
1876	11,461,150	.45	.55	.75	2.10
1876CC	8,270,000	.90	1.20	1.75	3.50
1876S	10,420,000	.75	1.15	1.75	3.00
1877	7,310,510	.50	.70	1.00	2.85
1877CC	7,700,000	.75	.95	1.25	2.85
1877S	2,340,000	.75	.95	1.25	2.85
1878	1,678,800	.75	.95	1.25	2.85
1878CC	200,000	5.50	7.75	12.00	19.00
1879	15,100	2.40	3.00	4.00	6.25
1880	37,355	2.75	3.65	5.00	7.25
1881	24,975	3.25	4.50	6.25	8.25
1882	3,911,100	.50	.70	1.00	2.25
1883	7,675,712	.50	.70	1.00	2.25
1884	3,366,380	.50	.70	1.00	2.35
1884S	564,969	3.50	4.75	6.50	14.00
1885	2,533,427	.45	.70	1.00	2.25
1885S	43,690	30.00	39.00	55.00	110.00
1886	6,377,570	.45	.65	1.00	2.25
1886S	206,524	3.50	4.75	7.00	14.00
1887	11,283,939	.45	.70	1.00	2.25

DIMES

	Quan. Minted	Good	V. Good	Fine	V. Fine
1887S	4,454,450	$1.00	$1.40	$2.00	$4.00
1888	5,496,487	.45	.70	1.00	2.25
1888S	1,720,000	1.40	1.85	2.50	4.00
1889	7,380,711	.45	.70	1.00	2.25
1889S	972,678	3.75	5.50	7.50	24.00
1890	9,911,541	.45	.70	1.00	2.50
1890S	1,423,076	.75	1.05	1.65	4.00
1891	15,310,600	.45	.70	1.00	2.50
1891O	4,540,000	1.10	1.55	2.25	7.25
1891S	3,196,116	.90	1.20	1.65	4.25

Good — Date and letters plain. *LIBERTY*
over brow is obliterated.

Fine — All letters in *L I B E R T Y* visible
though some are weak.

	Quan. Minted	Good	Fine
1892	12,121,245	.20	.75
1892O	3,841,700	.65	1.75
1892S	990,710	7.50	12.50
1893	3,340,792	.45	.75
1893O	1,760,000	1.50	4.00
1893S	2,491,401	1.50	4.00
1894	1,330,972	.75	2.00
1894O	720,000	12.00	32.50
1894S	24		
1895	690,880	10.00	20.00
1895O	440,000	22.00	60.00
1895S	1,120,000	3.00	8.75
1896	2,000,762	.80	1.00
1896O	610,000	6.50	20.00
1896S	575,056	12.00	22.00
1897	10,869,264	.20	.75
1897O	666,000	7.50	20.00
1897S	1,342,844	2.50	7.50
1898	16,320,735	.20	.75
1898O	2,130,000	1.25	4.00
1898S	1,702,507	1.00	3.25
1899	19,580,846	.15	.60
1899O	2,650,000	1.00	3.50
1899S	1,867,493	1.00	3.50
1900	17,600,912	.15	.50
1900O	2,010,000	1.00	3.50
1900S	5,168,270	.65	2.50
1901	18,860,478	.15	.60
1901O	5,620,000	.40	2.00
1901S	593,022	9.00	37.50
1902	21,380,777	.15	.60
1902O	4,500,000	.30	2.00
1902S	2,070,000	1.00	4.00
1903	19,500,755	.15	.35
1903O	8,180,000	.25	2.00
1903S	613,300	3.00	6.50
1904	14,601,027	.15	.30

DIMES

	Quan. Minted	Good	Fine
1904S	800,000	$3.00	$6.75
1905	14,552,350	.15	.30
1905O	3,400,000	.40	2.00
1905S	6,855,199	.35	2.00
1906	19,958,406	.10	.25
1906D	4,060,000	.25	.75
1906O	2,610,000	.15	1.00
1906S	3,136,640	.15	1.00
1907	22,220,575	.10	.20
1907D	4,080,000	.15	1.00
1907O	5,058,000	.20	1.00
1907S	3,178,470	.15	1.00
1908	10,600,545	.10	.25
1908D	7,490,000	.15	.65
1908O	1,789,000	.25	1.00
1908S	3,220,000	.30	1.00
1909	10,240,650	.10	.20
1909D	954,000	.75	3.00
1909O	2,287,000	.75	3.50
1909S	1,000,000	.75	3.50
1910	11,520,551	.10	.15
1910D	3,490,000	.25	.50
1910S	1,240,000	.40	1.00
1911	18,870,543	.10	.15
1911D	11,209,000	.15	.50
1911S	3,520,000	.20	.75
1912	19,350,700	.10	.15
1912D	11,760,000	.15	.50
1912S	3,420,000	.20	.75
1913	19,760,622	.10	.15
1913S	510,000	2.50	13.00
1914	17,360,655	.10	.20
1914D	11,908,000	.10	.35
1914S	2,100,000	.30	.75
1915	5,620,450	.10	.35
1915S	960,000	.50	.75
1916 Old type	18,490,000	.10	.50
1916S Old type	5,820,000	.10	.50

Good — Letters and dates clear. Lines and diagonal bands in fasces are obliterated.

Fine — All sticks in fasces are defined. Diagonal bands worn at center high points only.

	Quan. Minted	Good	Fine
1916 New type (Mercury Head)	22,180,080	.10	.25
1916D New type	264,000	40.00	95.00
1916S New type	10,450,000	.10	.50
1917	55,230,000	.10	.20
1917D	9,402,000	.30	1.25
1917S	27,330,000	.10	.35
1918	26,680,000	.10	.30
1918D	22,674,800	.10	.75
1918S	19,300,000	.10	.75

DIMES

	Quan. Minted	Good	Fine
1919	35,740,000	$ .10	$ .40
1919D	9,939,000	.60	3.00
1919S	8,850,000	.60	3.00
1920	59,030,000	.10	.30
1920D	19,171,000	.20	1.00
1920S	13,820,000	.20	1.00
1921	1,230,000	5.50	15.00
1921D	1,080,000	9.00	18.50
1923	50,130,000	.10	.20
1923S	6,440,000	.40	1.25
1924	24,010,000	.10	.20
1924D	6,810,000	.20	3.00
1924S	7,120,000	.20	3.00
1925	25,610,000	.10	.20
1925D	5,117,000	.50	1.25
1925S	5,850,000	.20	.75
1926	32,160,000	.10	.20
1926D	6,828,000	.20	1.25
1926S	1,520,000	.75	4.00
1927	28,080,000	.10	.20
1927D	4,812,000	.35	1.75
1927S	4,770,000	.20	.90
1928	19,480,000	.10	.15
1928D	4,161,000	.20	.35
1928S	7,400,000	.20	.35
1929	25,970,000	.10	.20
1929D	5,034,000	.10	.25
1929S	4,730,000	.10	.25
1930	6,770,000	.10	.25
1930S	1,843,000	.65	1.25
1931	3,150,000	.40	.75
1931D	1,260,000	.85	2.50
1931S	1,800,000	.60	1.75
1934	24,080,000	.10	.10
1934D	6,772,000	.10	.10
1935	58,830,000	.10	.10
1935D	10,477,000	.10	.20
1935S	15,840,000	.10	.10
Proof quantities shown in parentheses			
1936 (4,130)	87,504,130	.10	.10
1936D	16,132,000	.10	.10
1936S	9,210,000	.10	.10
1937 (5,756)	56,865,756	.10	.10
1937D	14,146,000	.10	.10
1937S	9,740,000	.10	.10
1938 (8,728)	22,198,728	.10	.10
1938D	5,537,000	.10	.10
1938S	8,090,000	.10	.10
1939 (9,321)	67,749,321	.10	.10
1939D	24,394,000	.10	.10
1939S	10,540,000	.10	.10
1940 (11,827)	65,361,827	.10	.10
1940D	21,198,000	.10	.10
1940S	21,560,000	.10	.10
1941 (16,557)	175,106,557	.10	.10

DIMES

	Quan. Minted	Good	Fine
1941D	45,634,000	$ .10	$ .10
1941S	43,090,000	.10	.10
1942 (22,329)	205,432,329	.10	.10
1942 over 1 (see picture on page 14)		35.00	52.50
1942D	60,740,000	.10	.10
1942S	49,300,000	.10	.10
1943	191,710,000	.10	.10
1943D	71,949,000	.10	.10
1943S	60,400,000	.10	.10
1944	231,410,000	.10	.10
1944D	62,224,000	.10	.10
1944S	49,490,000	.10	.10
1945	159,130,000	.10	.10
1945D	40,245,000	.10	.10
1945S	41,920,000	.10	.10

ROOSEVELT DIMES

Good — Hairlines worn smooth. Date, legends and mottoes readable.

Fine—Torch flame smooth. Vertical lines in torch show, horizontal lines smooth.

	Quan. Minted	Good	Fine
1946	255,250,000	.10	.10
1946D	61,043,500	.10	.10
1946S	27,900,000	.10	.10
1947	121,520,000	.10	.10
1947D	46,835,000	.10	.10
1947S	34,840,000	.10	.10
1948	74,950,000	.10	.10
1948D	52,841,000	.10	.10
1948S	35,520,000	.10	.10
1949	30,940,000	.10	.15
1949D	26,034,000	.10	.10
1949S	13,510,000	.10	.35
1950 (51,386)	50,181,500	.10	.10
1950D	46,803,000	.10	.10
1950S	20,440,000	.10	.35
1951 (57,500)	103,937,602	.10	.10
1951D	52,191,800	.10	.10
1951S	31,630,000	.10	.35
1952 (81,980)	99,122,073	.10	.10
1952D	122,100,000	.10	.10
1952S	44,419,500	.10	.10
1953 (128,800)	53,618,920	.10	.10
1953D	136,433,000	.10	.10
1953S	39,180,000	.10	.10
1954 (233,300)	114,243,503	.10	.10
1954D	106,397,000	.10	.10
1954S	22,860,000	.10	.10
1955 (378,200)	12,828,381	.10	.15
1955D	13,959,000	.10	.10
1955S	18,510,000	.10	.10

Dimes prior to 1956 command a premium if in bright uncirculated condition.

ROOSEVELT DIMES

	Quan. Minted	Fine
1956 (669,384)	109,309,384	$ .10
1956D	108,015,100	.10
1957 (1,247,952)	161,407,952	.10
1957D	113,354,330	.10
1958 (875,652)	32,785,652	.10
1958D	136,564,600	.10
1959 (1,149,291)	86,929,291	.10
1959D	164,919,790	.10
1960 (1,691,602)	72,081,602	.10
1960D	200,160,400	.10
1961 (3,028,244)	93,730,000	.10
1961D	209,146,550	.10
1962 (3,218,019)	75,668,019	.10
1962D	334,948,380	.10
1963		.10
1963D		.10

TWENTY-CENT PIECES
(Coined from 1875 to 1878)

This series was a short-lived coinage experiment; soon after their appearance the populace complained about the similarity in design and size to the quarter-dollar. The 1876CC mint piece is a great rarity, only about ten being in existence. 1877 and 1878 were struck in proof only.

Good—LIBERTY on shield obliterated. Letters and date legible.

V. Good — At least 3 letters of LIBERTY show.

Fine — LIBERTY completely readable, but partly weak.

Very Fine — All letters of LIBERTY bold.

	Quan. Minted	Good	V. Good	Fine	V. Fine
1875	39,700	$6.50	$8.00	$12.00	$15.00
1875CC	133,290	6.50	8.00	13.00	20.00
1875S	1,155,000	5.00	6.00	9.00	12.50
1876	15,900	6.50	8.00	12.00	18.50
1876CC (Only about 10 known)	10,000				
1877 Proofs only	510			Proof	280.00
1878 Proofs only	600			Proof	190.00

QUARTER DOLLARS
(Coined from 1796 to date)

The first date, 1796, follows the pattern of the early half dimes and dimes by the absence of a mark of value. In 1804 a "25 C" was added to the reverse. This mark of value was used until 1838 when "Quar. Dol." appeared although there was sufficient room for a complete spelling of the denomination. It was not until the adoption of the Barber (erroneously called "Morgan") type in 1892 that the value is spelled out entirely.

The rarest quarters are those of 1823 and 1827. The 1823 date is recut over a 22.

QUARTER DOLLARS

Fair — Details clear enough to identify.

Good — Date readable. Bust outlined, but no detail.

V. Good—All but deepest drapery folds worn smooth. All hairlines but curls lack detail.

Fine — All drapery lines visible. Hair partly worn.

V. Fine — Only left side of drapery is indistinct.

	Quan. Minted	Fair	Good	V. Good	Fine	V. Fine
1796	5,894	$255.00	$425.00	$700.00	$1100.00	$1650.00

1804	6,738	50.00	75.00	125.00	225.00	365.00
1805	121,394	20.00	30.00	40.00	62.50	130.00
1806	206,124	13.50	23.50	35.00	45.00	115.00
1807	220,643	13.50	23.50	35.00	45.00	105.00

Fair — Details clear enough to identify.

Good—Date, letters and stars readable. Hair under headband smooth. Cap lines worn smooth.

V. Good — Rim well defined. Main details visible. Full LIBERTY on cap. Hair above eye nearly smooth.

Fine — All hairlines show but drapery has only part details. Shoulder clasp distinct.

V. Fine — All details show, but some wear. Clasp and ear sharp.

1815	69,232	6.00	9.00	14.00	23.00	55.00
1818	361,174	5.50	8.50	10.50	16.00	30.00
1819	144,000	5.50	8.50	11.50	18.00	32.00
1820	127,444	4.50	6.25	9.50	15.00	27.00
1821	216,851	4.50	6.25	9.50	15.00	27.00
1822 All kinds	64,080					
Rev. 25 over 50		60.00	75.00	100.00	170.00	210.00
Perfect dies		5.50	8.50	13.00	21.50	48.00
1823 All 3 over 2	17,800	230.00	400.00	500.00	700.00	1300.00
1824		7.50	10.50	14.50	20.00	35.00
1825	168,000	6.00	9.00	13.00	17.50	24.50
1827 All kinds	4,000					
Originals (Rare)						—
Restrikes (Rare)						—
1828	102,000	4.75	8.50	10.50	15.00	27.50

QUARTER DOLLARS

Good — Bust is well defined. Hair under headband is smooth. Date letters, stars readable. Scant rims.

V. Good — Details apparent but worn on high spots. Rim strong. Full LIBERTY.

Fine—All hairlnes visible. Drapery partly worn. Shoulder clasp distinct.

V. Fine — Only top spots worn. Clasp sharp. Ear distinct.

	Quan. Minted	Good	V. Good	Fine	V. Fine
1831	398,000	$2.00	$3.00	$4.50	$10.00
1832	320,000	2.00	3.00	4.50	10.00
1833	156,000	2.00	3.00	4.50	10.00
1834	286,000	2.00	3.00	4.50	10.00
1835	1,952,000	2.00	3.00	4.50	10.00
1836	472,000	2.00	3.00	4.50	10.00
1837	252,400	2.00	3.00	4.50	10.00
1838 All kinds	832,000	2.00	3.00	4.50	10.00

Good — Scant rim. LIBERTY on shield worn off. Date and letters readable.

V. Good — Rim fairly defined, at least 3 letters in LIBERTY evident.

Fine — LIBERTY complete, but partly weak.

V. Fine — LIBERTY strong.

1838 New type — Liberty Seated		2.25	4.00	6.75	11.75
1839	491,146	2.00	3.25	5.50	10.00
1840O All kinds	425,200	2.15	3.40	5.50	10.25
1840 Drapery to elbow	188,127	2.75	4.15	6.50	11.00
1840O Drapery to elbow		2.25	3.40	5.50	10.50
1841	120,000	6.25	8.25	11.25	18.50
1841O	452,000	2.00	2.65	3.75	8.75
1842	88,000	2.00	2.75	3.90	7.75
1842O	769,000	2.25	2.85	4.75	9.25
1843	645,600	1.75	2.50	3.75	6.75
1843O	968,000	1.75	2.50	3.75	6.85
1844	421,200	1.75	2.50	3.75	6.85
1844O	740,000	2.00	2.75	3.85	7.65
1845	922,000	1.65	2.25	3.50	6.75
1846	510,000	1.75	2.40	3.50	6.50
1847	734,000	1.75	2.40	3.50	5.00
1847O	368,000	2.00	2.75	4 00	6.25
1848	146,000	2.00	2.75	4.00	6.25
1849	340,000	1.65	2.25	3.50	5.50
1849O (Not mentioned in Director's report)		32.50	42.50	62.50	90.00
1850	190,800	2.00	2.85	4.25	8.00
1850O	412,000	1.75	2.40	3.50	7.00
1851	160,000	1 75	2.40	3.50	7.15
1851O	88,000	1.75	2.75	4.50	11.00
1852	177,060	1.75	2.75	4.50	9.25
1852O	96,000	3.25	4.50	6.50	13.75

QUARTER DOLLARS

	Quan. Minted	Good	V. Good	Fine	V. Fine
1853 All kinds	15,254,220				
3 over 2, without arrows and rays.					
Beware altered 1858		$25.00	$28.00	$47.50	$72.50
Perfect date, with arrows and rays.		2.00	2.65	3.75	7.00
1853O Arrows and rays	1,332,000	3.25	4.50	6.75	11.75
1854	12,380,000	1.50	2.00	2.75	4.25
1854O	1,484,000	1.65	2.10	3.00	6.50
1855	2,857,000	1.50	2.00	2.75	5.50
1855O	176,000	18.50	27.50	37.50	67.50
1855S	396,400	22.50	29.00	36.50	65.00

1856	7,264,000	1.40	1.65	2.00	3.50
1856O	968,000	1.50	1.90	2.50	4.50
1856S	286,000	8.50	12.50	18.50	37.50
1857	9,644,000	1.25	1.35	1.50	3.00
1857O	1,180,000	1.50	1.75	2.25	4.50
1857S	82,000	8.00	11.00	17.50	42.50
1858	7,368,000	1.50	1.90	2.50	4.00
1858O	520,000	2.00	2.50	3.25	5.50
1858S	121,000	12.50	15.00	20.00	40.00
1859	1,344,000	1.50	1.85	2.25	3.75
1859O	260,000	1.75	2.10	2.75	4.50
1859S	80,000	12.50	15.00	20.00	42.50
1860	805,400	1.25	1.65	2.15	4.00
1860O	388,000	1.50	1.90	2.65	4.50
1860S	56,000	8.00	9.50	13.00	32.50
1861	4,854,600	1.50	1.75	2.15	4.00
1861S	96,000	7.50	10.00	13.00	31.00
1862	932,550	1.25	1.50	2.00	3.65
1862S	67,000	5.75	6.75	8.50	25.00
1863	192,060	1.65	2.10	3.00	5.00
1864	94,070	1.50	1.90	2.50	4.75
1864S	20,000	6.50	7.75	10.00	26.00
1865	59,300	2.00	2.65	3.50	5.65
1865S	41,000	4.75	6.00	8.00	22.50
1866 No motto. (Rare.) 1 known					

QUARTER DOLLARS

	Quan. Minted	Good	V. Good	Fine	V. Fine
1866 With motto —					
(In God We Trust)........17,525	$ 2.65	$ 3.25	$ 4.65	$ 7.00
1866S With motto..............28,000	7.25	8.25	10.50	27.50
1867..........................20,625	2.25	2.85	4.25	6.00
1867S.........................48,000	6.75	8.25	11.25	27.50
1868..........................30,000	2.65	3.25	4.65	6.50
1868S.........................96,000	5.85	7.25	10.00	24.00
1869..........................16,600	2.65	3.00	5.65	8.75
1869S.........................76,000	5.85	7.25	10.00	24.00
1870..........................87,400	2.00	2.50	3.25	5.00
1870CC........................8,340	80.00	100.00	125.00	200.00
1871.........................171,232	1.65	1.85	2.50	3.85
1871CC.......................10,890	67.50	82.50	110.00	185.00
1871S........................30,900	4.90	7.25	12.25	27.50
1872.........................182,950	1.65	2.25	2.85	4.25
1872CC........................9,100	100.00	127.50	157.50	295.00
1872S........................103,000	10.00	12.25	17.50	31.00
1873 Without Arrows..........220,600	4.00	5.50	8.50	11.00
1873CC Without Arrows........4,000	210.00	300.00	475.00	625.00
1873 Arrows................1,263,700	10.00	12.50	17.50	28.00
1873CC Arrows................12,462	180.00	250.00	360.00	575.00
1873S Arrows................156,000	12.50	16.00	21.00	32.50
1874 Arrows.................471,900	10.00	12.50	17.50	27.50
1874S Arrows................392,000	14.00	19.00	24.00	35.00
(Arrows removed after 1874.)					
1875........................4,293,500	1.65	1.85	2.50	3.85
1875CC......................140,000	3.25	4.25	5.65	8.75
1875S.......................680,000	5.00	6.00	9.25	19.25
1876......................17,817,150	1.65	2.10	3.00	4.10
1876CC.....................4,944,000	1.85	2.25	3.25	5.50
1876S.....................8,596,000	1.65	2.10	3.00	4.25
1877.....................10,911,710	1.65	2.00	3.00	4.00
1877CC....................4,192,000	2.00	2.25	3.00	5.75
1877S.....................8,996,000	1.65	2.00	3.00	4.10
1878.....................2,260,800	1.65	2.10	3.00	4.25
1878CC.....................996,000	3.25	4.00	5.25	8.75
1878S......................140,000	75.00	110.00	160.00	235.00
1879........................14,700	9.00	10.00	12.75	15.50
1880........................14,955	8.00	8.50	10.00	12.00
1881........................12,975	8.50	9.75	12.25	14.00
1882........................16,300	8.00	9.00	11.25	13.00
1883........................15,439	8.00	9.00	11.75	13.75
1884.........................8,875	11.50	12.50	14.00	17.50
1885........................14,530	8.50	9.75	12.25	14.75
1886.........................5,886	16.50	18.75	25.00	31.00

QUARTER DOLLARS

	Quan. Minted	Good	V. Good	Fine	V. Fine
1887	10,710	$ 8.50	$ 9.75	$12.25	$14.75
1888	10,833	8.50	9.75	12.25	14.75
1888S	1,216,000	1.65	2.00	2.85	5.25
1889	12,711	8.50	9.50	12.00	14.00
1890	80,590	2.00	2.50	3.50	5.50
1891	3,920,600	1.65	2.15	3.25	4.65
1891O	68,000	50.00	60.00	72.50	125.00
(Only date of this type struck at New Orleans Mint.)					
1891S	2,216,000	1.65	2.00	3.00	5.00

Good — Date and legends read-able. LIBERTY worn off on headband.

Fine — LIBERTY completely readable but not sharp.

	Quan. Minted	Good	Fine
1892	8,237,245	$ .40	$ .65
1892O	2,640,000	.80	2.50
1892S	964,079	4.00	12.00
1893	5,444,815	.40	.75
1893O	3,396,000	.60	2.00
1893S	1,454,535	1.00	3.25
1894	3,432,972	.40	.75
1894O	2,852,000	.60	2.25
1894S	2,648,821	.70	2.50
1895	4,440,880	.40	.65
1895O	2,816,000	.70	2.00
1895S	1,764,681	1.00	3.00
1896	3,874,762	.40	.75
1896O	1,484,000	1.25	7.00
1896S	188,039	40.00	110.00
1897	8,140,731	.40	.65
1897O	1,414,800	2.50	8.00
1897S	542,229	3.00	8.75
1898	11,100,735	.30	.50
1898O	1,868,000	.75	2.75
1898S	1,020,592	.85	2.75
1899	12,624,846	.30	.50
1899O	2,644,000	.75	2.50
1899S	708,000	2.25	5.25
1900	10,016,912	.35	.50
1900O	3,416,000	.90	4.00
1900S	1,858,585	.60	3.00
1901	8,892,813	.35	.50
1901O	1,612,000	3.00	16.00
1901S	72,664	92.50	250.00
1902	12,197,744	.35	.50
1902O	4,748,000	.60	3.25
1902S	1,524,612	1.00	4.50

QUARTER DOLLARS

	Quan. Minted	Good	Fine
1903	9,670,064	$ .30	$ .50
1903O	3,500,000	.65	5.00
1903S	1,036,000	1.25	5.75
1904	9,588,813	.35	.50
1904O	2,456,000	1.75	7.00
1905	4,968,250	.35	.50
1905O	1,230,000	1.25	6.00
1905S	1,884,000	1.00	3.25
1906	3,656,435	.35	.50
1906D	3,280,000	.40	.90
1906O	2,056,000	.40	1.00
1907	7,192,575	.35	.50
1907D	2,484,000	.35	.80
1907O	4,560,000	.35	.80
1907S	1,360,000	.40	1.75
1908	4,232,545	.30	.50
1908D	5,788,000	.30	.60
1908O	6,244,000	.30	.60
1908S	784,000	1.25	3.75
1909	9,268,650	.30	.50
1909D	5,114,000	.30	.60
1909O	712,000	5.00	17.50
1909S	1,348,000	.50	1.50
1910	2,244,551	.35	.70
1910D	1,500,000	.50	.70
1911	3,720,543	.30	.50
1911D	933,600	.65	2.50
1911S	988,000	.65	2.50
1912	4,400,700	.30	.50
1912S	708,000	.90	3.25
1913	484,613	1.20	2.50
1913D	1,450,800	.35	1.50
1913S	40,000	40.00	110.00
1914	6,244,610	.30	.50
1914D	3,046,000	.30	.60
1914S	264,000	1.50	8.00
1915	3,480,450	.30	.70
1915D	3,694,000	.30	.50
1915S	704,000	.65	1.75
1916	1,788,000	.30	1.00
1916D	6,540,800	.25	.85

Good — Date and lettering readable. Top of date worn. Liberty's right leg and toes worn off. Left leg and drapery lines show much wear.

Fine — High curve of her right leg flat from thigh to ankle. Left leg shows only slight wear. Drapery lines over right knee seen only at sides of leg.

(Some modifications must be made for grading variety 2.)

		Good	Fine
1916 Liberty standing	52,000	100.00	225.00
1917 Stars at sides of eagle	8,792,000	1.25	1.75

QUARTER DOLLARS

	Quan. Minted	Good	Fine
1917D Stars at sides of eagle	1,509,200	$ 1.50	$ 3.75
1917S Stars at sides of eagle	1,952,000	1.75	4.00

1917 3 stars below eagle	13,880,000	1.00	2.25
1917D 3 stars below eagle	6,224,400	2.25	6.00
1917S 3 stars below eagle	5,552,000	2.25	6.00
1918	14,240,000	1.25	3.50
1918D	7,380,000	2.00	4.50
1918S All kinds	11,072,000	1.25	4.00
1918S 8 over 7 (See page 13)		100.00	225.00
1919	11,324,000	1.25	3.50
1919D	1,944,000	6.50	17.50
1919S	1,836,000	12.00	22.50
1920	27,860,000	.85	2.00
1920D	3,586,400	2.75	9.00
1920S	6,380,000	1.50	4.00
1921	1,916,000	7.50	15.00
1923	9,716,000	.85	2.00
1923S*	1,360,000	12.50	25.00
1924	10,920,000	.85	2.00
1924D	3,112,000	1.25	3.00
1924S	2,860,000	2.00	4.50
1925	12,280,000	.35	1.00
1926	11,316,000	.35	1.00
1926D	1,716,000	.35	1.00
1926S	2,700,000	1.00	4.00
1927	11,912,000	.50	1.00
1927D	976,400	.75	1.00
1927S	396,000	2.50	6.00
1928	6,336,000	.40	.50
1928D	1,627,600	.40	.50
1928S	2,644,000	.40	.50
1929	11,140,000	.40	.50
1929D	1,358,000	.40	.50
1929S	1,764,000	.40	.50
1930	5,632,000	.40	.50
1930S	1,556,000	.40	.50

Liberty standing quarters minted from 1916 to 1924 are scarce in any condition. The quarters struck during this period had the date in the same position as later issues, but because that part of the coin was high it received much wear and after a few years in circulation became obliterated. Since 1924 the date has been "recessed," thereby permitting coin to wear and date remain legible.

*Beware altered date.

QUARTER DOLLARS

Quarters dated prior to 1956 command a premium if in bright uncirculated condition.

V. Good — Wing-tips outlined. Rims on both sides are fine and even. Tops of letters at rim are flattened.
V. Fine — Hair details worn but plain. Feathers at sides of eagle's breast are plain.
Proof totals shown in parentheses.

	Quan. Minted	Very Good	Very Fine		Quan. Minted	Very Fine
1932	5,404,000	$ .25	$ .25	1947	22,556,000	$ .25
1932D	436,800	3.25	10.00	1947D	15,338,400	.25
1932S	408,000	3.00	6.50	1947S	5,532,000	.25
1934	31,912,052	.25	.25	1948	35,196,000	.25
1934D	3,527,200	.40	1.00	1948D	16,766,800	.25
1935	32,484,000	.25	.25	1948S	15,960,000	.25
1935D	5,780,000	.40	1.00	1949	9,312,000	.25
1935S	5,660,000	.40	1.00	1949D	10,068,400	.25
1936 (3,837)	41,303,837	.25	.25	1950 (51,386)	24,971,512	.25
1936D	5,374,000	2.00	5.00	1950D	21,075,600	.25
1936S	3,828,000	.25	1.00	1950S	10,284,004	.25
1937 (5,542)	19,701,542	.25	.25	1951 (57,500)	43,505,602	.25
1937D	7,189,600	.25	.25	1951D	35,354,800	.25
1937S	1,652,000	.75	2.00	1951S	8,948,000	.25
1938 (8,045)	9,480,045	.25	2.50	1952 (81,980)	38,862,073	.25
1938S	2,832,000	.25	.60	1952D	49,795,200	.25
1939 (8,795)	33,548,795	.25	.25	1952S	13,707,800	.25
1939D	7,092,000	.25	.25	1953 (128,800)	18,664,920	.25
1939S	2,628,000	.25	.25	1953D	56,112,400	.25
1940(11,246)	35,715,246	.25	.25	1953S	14,016,000	.25
1940D	2,797,600	.25	1.00	1954 (233,300)	54,645,503	.25
1940S	8,244,000	.25	.25	1954D	46,305,500	.25
1941(15,287)	79,047,287	.25	.25	1954S	11,834,722	.25
1941D	16,714,800	.25	.25	1955 (378,200)	18,558,381	.25
1941S	16,080,000	.25	.25	1955D	3,182,400	.25
1942 (21,123)				1956 (669,384)	44,813,384	.25
	102,117,123	.25	.25	1956D	32,334,500	.25
1942D	17,487,200	.25	.25	1957 (1,247,952)	47,779,952	.25
1942S	19,384,000	.25	.25	1957D	77,924,160	.25
1943	99,700,000	.25	.25	1958 (875,652)	7,235,652	.25
1943D	16,095,600	.25	.25	1958D	78,124,900	.25
1943S	21,700,000	.25	.25	1959 (1,149,291)	25,533,291	.25
1944	104,956,000	.25	.25	1959D	62,054,232	.25
1944D	14,600,000	.25	.25	1960 (1,691,602)	30,855,602	.25
1944S	12,560,000	.25	.25	1960D	63,000,324	.25
1945	74,372,000	.25	.25	1961 (3,028,244)	37,036,000	.25
1945D	12,341,600	.25	.25	1961D	83,656,928	.25
1945S	17,004,001	.25	.25	1962 (3,218,019)	39,374,019	.25
1946	53,436,000	.25	.25	1962D	127,554,756	.25
1946D	9,072,800	.25	.25	1963		.25
1946S	4,204,000	.25	.25	1963D		.25

HALF DOLLARS
(Coined from 1794 to date)

A series that has been extensively collected by "varieties" and many dates contain both rare and common varieties. The collector who cares to go into the study of half dollar varieties should obtain a copy of "Haseltine's Type-Table" or Beistle's work on half dollars.

Half dollars between about 1812 and 1840 are more or less common in ordinary circulated condition. This might be explained by the fact that the U. S. government did not issue silver dollars during this period which made the half the "big" silver money and coinage was plentiful according to standards of the time.

1796 and 1797 are the rarest of the early dates. The 1838O mint is excessively rare (only 20 coined). Only 3 or 4 specimens are known of the 1853 without arrows at the date or rays through the eagle. This rarity has been faked by removing the arrows and rays from the common variety 1853. Several of the Liberty Standing type half dollars are scarce in uncirculated condition.

Fair — Clear enough to identify.

Good — Date and letters sufficient to be readable. Main devices outlined, but lack details.

V. Gd.—Major details discernible. Letters well formed but worn.

Fine — Hair ends distinguishable. Top hairlines show, but otherwise worn smooth.

V. Fine — Hair in center shows some detail. Other details more bold.

	Quan. Minted	Fair	Good	V. Good	Fine	V. Fine
1794	5,300	$67.50	$120.00	$190.00	$275.00	$525.00
1795 All kinds	317,836					
Re-engraved date, 3 leaves under wings		67.50	175.00	275.00	425.00	625.00
Perfect date, 2 leaves under wings		37.00	52.50	70.00	100.00	200.00

Grading same as above for Fair to Fine.

V. Fine — Right side of drapery slightly worn. Left side to curls is smooth.

		Fair	Good	V. Good	Fine	V. Fine
1796 All kinds (Quantity minted not given in Director's report.)						
15 stars		380.00	575.00	850.00	1450.00	2000.00
16 stars		385.00	700.00	1000.00	1500.00	2100.00
1797	3,918	325.00	575.00	775.00	1200.00	1750.00

HALF DOLLARS

Good — Letters and date readable. E. PLURIBUS UNUM obliterated.

V. Good — Motto partially readable. Only deepest drapery details visible. All other lines smooth.

Fine — All drapery lines distinguishable. Hairlines near cheek and neck show some detail.

V. Fine — Left side of drapery worn smooth.

	Quan. Minted	Good	V. Good	Fine	V. Fine
1801	30,289	$37.50	$62.50	$90.00	$150.00
1802	29,890	27.50	45.00	60.00	110.00
1803	31,715	13.50	22.00	30.00	65.00
1805 All kinds	211,722				
5 over 4		19.00	27.50	42.50	72.50
Perfect date		8.25	12.00	20.00	39.00
1806 over 5		14.00	17.25	26.00	51.00
1806 over inverted 6		28.00	37.50	62.50	125.00
1806	839,576	8.50	10.50	20.00	37.50
1807 Face to right	301,076	8.50	10.50	20.00	37.50

Good — Date and letters readable. Bust worn smooth with outline distinct.

V. Good — LIBERTY visible but faint. Legends distinguishable. Clasp at shoulder visible. Curl above it nearly smooth.

Fine — Clasp and adjacent curl clearly outlined with slight details.

V. Fine — Clasp at shoulder clear. Curl has wear only on highest point. Hair over brow distinguishable.

1807 Face to left	750,500	3.75	5.50	9.50	20.00
1808 over 7		3.25	5.00	8.50	12.50
1808	1,368,600	2.00	2.75	4.50	7.85
1809	1,405,810	2.00	2.65	4.00	7.85
1810	1,276,276	2.00	2.65	4.00	7.25
1811	1,203,644	2.00	3.25	6.00	9.00
1812 over 11		4.00	5.50	8.50	24.00
1812	1,628,059	1.75	2.40	3.75	6.25
1813	1,241,903	1.75	2.40	3.75	6.75
1814 over 13		4.50	6.25	10.25	18.00
1814	1,039,075	2.00	3.00	4.50	6.75
1815 over 12	47,150	32.50	40.00	65.00	85.00
1817 over 13		5.00	7.00	12.50	20.00

HALF DOLLARS

	Quan. Minted	Good	V. Good	Fine	V. Fine
1817 dated 181.7		$ 4.75	$ 8.00	$14.00	$21.00
1817	1,215,567	2.00	2.75	4.50	8.00
1818 over 17		2.00	2.75	4.50	8.00
1818	1,960,322	1.50	2.10	3.35	5.75
1819 over 18		1.75	2.40	3.65	7.25
1819	2,208,000	1.75	2.25	3.65	6.75
1820 over 19		3.50	4.50	6.75	12.25
1820	751,122	3.25	4.00	5.65	11.25
1821	1,305,797	1.65	2.00	3.10	5.25
1822 over 21		16.00	22.50	37.50	45.00
1822	1,559,573	1.50	1.90	2.75	5.25
1823	1,694,200	1.75	2.25	3.50	5.25
1824 over 21		2.00	2.65	4.25	6.75
1824 over other dates		2.25	3.15	5.00	7.25
1824	3,504,954	1.75	2.15	3.10	4.50
1825	2,943,166	1.75	2.15	3.10	4.25
1826	4,004,180	1.75	2.15	3.10	4.25
1827 over 26		4.75	6.50	10.50	19.50
1827	5,493,400	1.40	1.90	3.10	4.00
1828	3,075,200	2.00	2.40	3.10	4.00
1828 Curled-base, knobbed 2		14.00	18.50	27.00	41.00
1829 over 21		2.25	2.65	5.00	8.00
1829	3,712,156	2.00	2.35	3.10	4.00
1830	4,764,800	1.50	1.80	2.50	4.00
1831	5,873,660	1.25	1.65	2.50	4.00
1832	4,797,000	1.25	1.65	2.50	4.00
1833	5,206,000	1.50	1.80	2.50	4.00
1834	6,412,004	1.25	1.65	2.50	4.00
1835	5,352,006	1.25	1.65	2.50	4.00
1836 All kinds Lettered edge	6,546,200	1.25	1.65	2.50	4.00

Good—LIBERTY discernible on headband.

V. Gd.—Minimum of 3 letters in LIBERTY must be clear.

Fine—LIBERTY complete.

V.F.—LIBERTY is sharp. Shoulder clasp is clear.

1836 Reeded edge		22.50	35.00	50.00	75.00
1837	3,629,820	4.75	7.50	12.50	18.00

Not mentioned in Director's report. (Rufus Tyler, coiner of New Orleans Mint, stated that only 20 were coined.)

First branch mint half dollar. This and following year mint-mark appears on Obv. All other years (except 1916-17) mint-mark is on Rev.

HALF DOLLARS

	Quan. Minted	Good	V. Good	Fine	V. Fine
1838	3,546,000	$ 4.75	$ 7.50	$ 12.50	$ 17.50
1838O	(20)				
1839 All kinds	3,334,560	4.25	6.50	12.00	17.50
1839O All kinds	162,976	27.50	40.00	60.00	75.00

Gd.–Scant rim. *LIBERTY* on shield worn off. Date and letters readable.

V.G.—*Rim fairly defined. At least 3 letters in LIBERTY are evident.*

Fine–*LIBERTY* complete, but weak.

V. Fine—*LIBERTY* mostly sharp.

	Quan. Minted	Good	V. Good	Fine	V. Fine
1839 Liberty seated		3.50	4.50	6.75	12.50
1840	1,435,008	2.00	2.75	4.50	6.75
1840O	855,100	1.75	2.20	3.40	5.65
1841	310,000	2.50	3.50	5.75	10.00
1841O	401,000	2.00	2.40	3.40	5.65
1842	2,012,764	1.65	2.05	3.10	5.65
1842O Large date All kinds	957,000	1.65	2.05	3.10	5.65
1842O Small date		27.50	37.50	57.50	70.00
1843	3,844,000	1.65	2.05	3.10	5.65
1843O	2,268,000	1.65	2.05	3.10	5.25
1844	1,766,000	1.65	2.05	3.10	5.25
1844O	2,005,000	1.65	2.05	3.10	5.25
1845	589,000	1.65	2.05	3.10	5.25
1845O	2,094,000	1.65	2.05	3.10	5.25
1845O No Drapery		9.50	15.00	22.50	42.50
1846 All kinds	2,210,000				
Over horizontal 6 (error)		17.50	27.50	42.50	70.00
Perfect date		1.50	2.00	3.10	5.25
1846O	2,304,000	1.50	1.90	2.75	5.25
1847 over 46		67.50	95.00	145.00	585.00
1847	1,156,000	1.50	2.15	3.40	6.25
1847O	2,584,000	1.50	2.15	3.40	5.65
1848	580,000	1.50	2.15	3.40	6.25
1848O	3,180,000	1.25	1.90	3.10	5.65
1849	1,252,000	1.50	2.15	3.40	6.25
1849O	2,310,000	1.50	1.90	2.75	5.25
1850	227,000	12.50	16.00	22.50	40.00
1850O	2,456,000	2.00	2.75	4.50	6.25
1851	200,750	3.75	5.25	9.00	28.00
1851O	402,000	1.65	2.10	3.40	5.65
1852	77,130	12.50	16.00	25.00	77.50
1852O	144,000	8.50	11.00	17.00	41.00
1853O All kinds	1,328,000				
No arrows or rays. (Ex. rare) Beware 1858-O altered date		——	——	——	——

HALF DOLLARS

Arrows
at
Date
1853
to
1855

Rays
Around
Eagle
1853
Only

	Quan. Minted	Good	V. Good	Fine	V. Fine
1853O Arrows and rays		$ 2.75	$ 4.50	$ 8.50	$12.50
1853 Arrows and rays	3,532,708	2.25	3.75	7.00	11.25
1854 Arrows, no Rays	2,982,000	1.50	2.25	3.75	5.65
1854O Arrows, no Rays	5,240,000	1.50	2.25	3.75	5.65
1855 Arrows, no Rays	759,500	2.00	2.65	4.25	6.25
1855O Arrows, no Rays	3,688,000	1.25	2.15	4.00	6.00
1855S Arrows, no Rays	129,950	17.00	28.00	50.00	102.50

		Good	V. Good	Fine	V. Fine
1856	938,000	.90	1.40	2.50	4.50
1856O	2,658,000	.90	1.40	2.50	4.50
1856S	211,000	5.00	7.50	12.50	42.50
1857	1,988,000	.90	1.40	2.50	4.50
1857O	818,000	1.50	2.00	3.10	5.65
1857S	158,000	8.00	12.00	19.50	42.50
1858	4,226,000	.80	1.25	2.25	4.00
1858O	7,294,000	.80	1.25	2.25	4.00
1858S	476,000	3.00	5.50	9.75	17.00
1859	748,000	.80	1.25	2.25	4.25
1859O	2,834,000	.80	1.25	2.25	4.25
1859S	566,000	4.00	5.75	10.00	17.00
1860	303,700	.80	1.25	2.25	4.25
1860O	1,290,000	.80	1.25	2.25	4.25
1860S	472,000	2.00	3.15	5.75	10.75
1861	2,888,400	.80	1.25	2.25	4.25
1861O	330,000	1.00	1.50	2.85	5.65

Struck at the New Orleans Mint after it was taken over by the Confederate States:

1861O For Louisiana 1,240,000
1861O For Confederacy 962,633

As all these 1861O coins were struck from U.S. dies it is impossible to distinguish one from another. Not to be confused with the very rare Confederate half dollar of 1861 which has a distinctive reverse.

HALF DOLLARS

	Quan. Minted	Good	V. Good	Fine	V. Fine
1861 Confederate Reverse (Restrike)....					
1861S	939,500	$ 1.50	$ 2.40	$ 4.50	$ 8.50
1862	252,350	1.25	1.90	3.40	5.00
1862S	1,352,000	1.40	1.90	3.40	10.75
1863	503,660	1.25	1.90	3.40	5.65
1863S (With small S only)	916,000	1.15	1.90	3.40	6.25
1864	379,570	1.25	1.90	3.40	5.65
1864S	658,000	1.15	1.90	3.40	6.25
1865	511,900	1.15	1.90	3.40	5.65
1865S	675,000	1.15	1.90	3.10	5.65
1866S	1,054,000	20.00	30.00	50.00	95.00

	Quan. Minted	Good	V. Good	Fine	V. Fine
1866 Motto — "In God We Trust"	745,625	1.75	2.50	4.50	6.75
1866S		1.75	2.40	3.85	8.50
1867	424,325	1.65	2.15	3.40	6.25
1867S	1,196,000	1.10	1.65	2.85	7.75
1868	378,200	1.65	2.15	3.40	6.25
1868S	1,160,000	1.10	1.65	2.85	6.25
1869	795,900	1.40	1.75	2.85	5.00
1869S	656,000	1.10	1.65	2.85	5.25
1870	600,900	1.10	1.65	2.85	5.00
1870CC	54,617	27.50	37.50	57.50	115.00
1870S	1,004,000	1.50	2.25	3.85	11.25
1871	1,165,360	1.10	1.65	2.85	4.85
1871CC	139,950	22.50	35.00	57.50	102.50
1871S	2,178,000	1.40	2.40	3.85	7.75
1872	881,550	1.10	1.65	2.85	4.50
1872CC	272,000	15.00	24.00	36.00	57.50
1872S	580,000	1.65	3.25	8.50	11.25
1873 Without Arrows	801,800	1.50	2.25	4.00	5.65
1873 With Arrows	1,815,700	10.00	13.50	21.00	35.00
1873CC Without Arrows	122,500	20.00	32.50	50.00	70.00
1873CC With Arrows	214,560	14.00	22.50	35.00	47.50
1873S Without Arrows (Unknown)	5,000				
1873S With Arrows	228,000	13.00	17.50	27.50	42.50
1874 With Arrows	2,360,300	9.50	13.00	20.00	35.00
1874CC With Arrows	59,000	17.50	27.50	55.00	90.00
1874S With Arrows	394,000	13.00	17.50	27.50	42.50
1875	6,027,500	1.10	1.65	2.85	4.25
1875CC	1,008,000	2.50	3.00	4.50	11.25
1875S	3,200,000	1.25	1.75	2.85	4.25

HALF DOLLARS

	Quan. Minted	Good	V. Good	Fine	V. Fine
1876	8,419,150	$ 1.00	$ 1.45	$ 2.50	$ 4.00
1876CC	1,956,000	2.00	2.75	4.50	8.50
1876S	4,528,000	1.00	1.45	2.50	4.00
1877	8,304,510	1.00	1.45	2.50	4.00
1877CC	1,420,000	2.00	2.75	5.00	8.50
1877S	5,356,000	1.00	1.45	2.50	4.00
1878	1,378,400	1.00	1.45	2.50	4.00
1878CC	62,000	45.00	57.50	77.50	125.00
1878S	12,000	130.00	175.00	255.00	530.00
1879	5,900	5.50	7.50	12.25	16.75
1880	9,755	8.50	11.00	16.00	20.00
1881	10,975	8.50	11.00	16.00	20.00
1882	5,500	8.50	11.00	16.00	20.00
1883	9,039	8.50	10.50	15.00	19.50
1884	5,275	9.50	11.00	16.25	21.00
1885	6,130	9.50	11.00	16.25	21.00
1886	5,886	11.00	13.50	18.50	23.00
1887	5,710	9.00	11.00	15.00	19.50
1888	12,833	8.50	10.50	13.50	16.75
1889	12,711	8.50	10.50	13.50	16.75
1890	12,590	8.50	10.50	13.50	17.75
1891	200,600	2.00	2.40	3.40	6.25

Good — Date and legends readable. LIBERTY worn off on headband.

Fine — LIBERTY completely readable, but not sharp.

	Quan. Minted	Good	Fine
1892	935,245	.85	2.50
1892O	390,000	12.00	17.50
1892S	1,029,028	12.00	20.00
1893	1,826,792	.85	1.75
1893O	1,389,000	2.25	4.75
1893S	740,000	9.00	17.50
1894	1,148,972	.75	1.75
1894O	2,138,000	1.00	5.00
1894S	4,048,690	1.00	5.00
1895	1,835,218	.65	1.25
1895O	1,766,000	.75	3.00
1895S	1,108,086	1.90	5.50
1896	950,762	.70	1.50
1896O	924,000	1.50	6.00
1896S	1,140,948	10.00	20.00
1897	2,480,731	.60	1.25
1897O	632,000	10.00	20.00
1897S	933,900	10.00	20.00
1898	2,956,735	.60	.90
1898O	874,000	.90	2.25

HALF DOLLARS

	Quan. Minted	Good	Fine
1898S	2,358,550	$ .90	$ 2.25
1899	5,538,846	.65	.90
1899O	1,724,000	.75	2.25
1899S	1,686,411	.75	2.25
1900	4,762,912	.60	.75
1900O	2,744,000	.65	1.25
1900S	2,560,322	.75	1.25
1901	4,268,813	.65	.70
1901O	1,124,000	.90	5.50
1901S	847,044	2.50	23.00
1902	4,922,777	.55	.75
1902O	2,526,000	.65	2.00
1902S	1,460,670	.65	2.25
1903	2,278,755	.60	.75
1903O	2,100,000	.60	1.50
1903S	1,920,772	1.00	3.00
1904	2,992,670	.60	.75
1904O	1,117,600	.75	2.25
1904S	553,038	2.75	11.50
1905	662,727	.55	1.60
1905O	505,000	.75	4.50
1905S	2,494,000	.75	1.50
1906	2,638,675	.55	.75
1906D	4,028,000	.55	.90
1906O	2,446,000	.55	1.50
1906S	1,740,154	.60	1.75
1907	2,598,575	.55	.75
1907D	3,856,000	.55	.75
1907O	3,946,600	.60	.90
1907S	1,250,000	.60	1.50
1908	1,354,545	.55	1.25
1908D	3,280,000	.55	1.25
1908O	5,360,000	.55	1.25
1908S	1,644,828	.60	1.50
1909	2,368,650	.55	.75
1909O	925,400	.60	2.00
1909S	1,764,000	.60	1.25
1910	418,551	.65	1.25
1910S	1,948,000	.55	1.00
1911	1,406,543	.55	.75
1911D	695,080	.55	.90
1911S	1,272,000	.60	.90
1912	1,550,700	.55	.75
1912D	2,300,800	.55	.75
1912S	1,370,000	.60	1.00
1913	188,627	3.00	12.50
1913D	534,000	.60	2.25
1913S	604,000	1.00	2.25
1914	124,610	3.50	20.00
1914S	992,000	.60	.90
1915	138,450	4.00	20.00
1915D	1,170,400	.60	.75
1915S	1,604,000	.60	.75

Liberty Head Half Dollars, 1892-1915, have been referred to as the "Morgan" type. An injustice to the actual designer, Charles E. Barber.

HALF DOLLARS

V. Good — Motto is distinct. About half of skirt lines at left are clear.

Fine — All skirt lines evident, but worn in spots. Details in sandal above date are clear.

V. Fine — Lines on skirt incomplete. Lines in sandal complete but

not bold. Some wear on breast and arm.

Proof totals shown in parentheses.

	Quan. Minted	V. Good	Fine
1916	608,000	$1.00	$ 2.00
1916D on Obv	1,014,400	1.00	2.25
1916S on Obv	508,000	2.25	7.50
1917	12,292,000	.50	.55
1917D on Obv	765,400	1.00	2.50
1917D on Rev	1,940,000	.75	2.00
1917S on Obv	952,000	1.50	10.00
1917S on Rev	5,554,000	.55	1.35
1918	6,634,000	.50	.75
1918D	3,853,040	.55	.90
1918S	10,282,000	.55	.90
1919	962,000	1.50	3.50
1919D	1,165,000	1.50	3.50
1919S	1,552,000	2.50	12.50
1920	6,372,000	.50	.50
1920D	1,551,000	.50	2.00
1920S	4,624,000	.50	2.00
1921	246,000	5.00	13.00
1921D	208,000	5.00	13.00
1921S	548,000	1.00	3.00
1923S	2,178,000	.50	.75
1927S	2,392,000	.50	.65
1928S	1,940,000	.50	.60
1929D	1,001,200	.50	.60
1929S	1,902,000	.50	.60
1933S	1,786,000	.50	.60
1934	6,964,000	.50	.50
1934D	2,361,400	.50	.50
1934S	3,652,000	.50	.60
1935	9,162,000	.50	.50
1935D	3,003,800	.50	.60
1935S	3,854,000	.50	.60
1936 (3,901)	12,617,901	.50	.50
1936D	4,252,400	.50	.50
1936S	3,884,000	.50	.60
1937 (5,728)	9,527,728	.50	.50
1937D	1,760,001	.50	.60

HALF DOLLARS

	Quan. Minted	V. Fine		Quan. Minted	V. Fine
1937S	2,090,000	$1.00	1943	53,190,000	$ .50
1938 (8,152)	4,118,152	.50	1943D	11,346,000	.50
1938D	491,600	3.00	1943S	13,450,000	.50
1939 (8,808)	6,820,808	.50	1944	28,206,000	.50
1939D	4,267,800	.50	1944D	9,769,000	.50
1939S	2,552,000	.55	1944S	8,904,000	.50
1940 (11,279)	9,167,279	.50	1945	31,502,000	.50
1940S	4,550,000	.50	1945D	9,966,800	.50
1941 (15,412)	24,207,412	.50	1945S	10,156,000	.50
1941D	11,248,400	.50	1946	12,118,000	.50
1941S	8,098,000	.50	1946D	2,151,100	.50
1942 (21,120)	47,839,120	.50	1946S	3,724,000	.50
1942D	10,973,800	.50	1947	4,094,000	.50
1942S	12,708,000	.50	1947D	3,900,600	.50

The designer was John R. Sinnock and his initials appear under the shoulder.

Halves dated prior to 1952 command a premium if in bright uncirculated condition.

Ex. Fine — Wear spots appear at top of end curls and hair back of ears. On reverse, Liberty Bell will show wear at top.

	Quan. Minted	Ex. Fine		Quan. Minted	Ex. Fine
1948	3,006,814	.60	1954S	4,993,400	.50
1948D	4,028,600	.50	1955 (378,200)	2,876,381	.50
1949	5,714,000	1.00	1956 (669,384)	4,701,384	.50
1949D	4,120,600	.50	1957 (1,247,952)	6,361,952	.50
1949S	3,744,000	.50	1957D	19,966,850	.50
1950 (51,386)	7,793,509	.50	1958 (875,652)	4,917,652	.50
1950D	8,031,600	.50	1958D	23,962,412	.50
1951 (57,500)	16,859,602	.50	1959 (1,149,291)	7,349,291	.50
1951D	9,475,200	.50	1959D	13,053,750	.50
1951S	13,696,000	.50	1960 (1,691,602)	7,715,602	.50
1952 (81,980)	21,274,073	.50	1960D	18,215,812	.50
1952D	25,395,600	.50	1961 (3,028,244)	8,290,000	.50
1952S	5,526,000	.50	1961D	20,276,442	.50
1953 (128,800)	2,796,920	.50	1962 (3,218,019)	12,932,019	.50
1953D	20,900,400	.50	1962D	35,473,281	.50
1953S	4,148,000	.50	1963		.50
1954 (233,300)	13,421,503	.50	1963D		.50
1954D	25,445,580	.50			

SILVER DOLLARS

(Coinage begun in 1794, last year coined 1935)

Major types of silver dollars are few, although the early dates are plentiful in die varieties. The first date, 1794, is quite rare. The bust type was adopted in the latter part of 1795 and all dates of this type are fairly common except one — the famous 1804. The 1804 silver dollar has been the most discussed coin in American numismatics. There are those that are called "originals" of which eight specimens are known, and those called "restrikes" of which seven specimens are known. Fake 1804's have been made by altering 1801's which are of the same general type; some of these altered dates are very cleverly done and almost defy detection.

Silver dollars of 1836, 1838 and 1839 are patterns. About 1,000 pieces of the common type 1836 were struck; of the other varieties only 3 to 18 were struck.

After 1840 all silver dollars are relatively common with exception of just a few dates, 1851, 1852, 1858, etc.

Fair — Clear enough to identify.

Good — Date and letters readable. Main devices outlined, but lack details.

V. Good — Major details discernible. Letters well formed but worn.

Fine — Hair ends distinguishable. Top hairlines show, but otherwise worn smooth.

V. Fine — Hair in center shows some detail. Other details more bold.

	Quan. Minted	Fair	Good	V. Good	Fine	V. Fine
1794	1,758	$300.00	$700.00	$1000.00	$1750.00	$3500.00
1795	184,013	35.00	45.00	60.00	85.00	150.00

Fair — Clear enough to identify.

Good — Bust outlined, no detail. Date readable, some leaves evident.

V. Good — Drapery worn except deepest folds. Hairlines smooth.

Fine — All drapery lines distinguishable. Hairlines near cheek and neck show some detail.

V. Fine — Left side of drapery worn smooth.

SILVER DOLLARS

	Quan. Minted	Fair	Good	V. Good	Fine	V. Fine
1795 Bust Type		$27.50	$42.50	$55.00	$80.00	$135.00
1796	72,920	25.00	40.00	50.00	75.00	125.00
1797	7,776	32.50	50.00	75.00	125.00	175.00
1798 All kinds	327,536					
Small eagle, 15 stars		28.00	35.00	60.00	80.00	150.00
Small eagle, 13 stars		28.00	40.00	65.00	85.00	155.00

Good — Letters and date readable. E. PLURIBUS UNUM obliterated.

V. Good — Motto partially readable. Only deepest drapery details visible. All other lines smooth.

Fine — All drapery lines distinguishable. Hairlines near cheek and neck show some detail.

V. Fine — Left side of drapery worn smooth.

1798 Heraldic eagle		15.00	22.50	37.50	60.00
1799	423,515	20.00	26.00	39.00	60.00
1800	220,920	20.00	24.00	35.00	60.00
1801	54,454	20.00	25.00	35.00	67.50
1802	41,650	18.00	22.50	27.50	42.50
1803	66,064	18.00	22.50	27.50	42.50

1804 Type 1, letter O in "OF"

Proof

above right half of cloud............................$20,000.00

Type 2, letter O in "OF"

above space between clouds........................... 20,000.00

SILVER DOLLARS

PATTERN SILVER DOLLARS

Owing to the interest in Pattern Silver Dollars of 1836, 1838 and 1839 we are including a list of them with the Dollars of regular issue. There was no regular issue of dollars 1805 to 1839 inclusive. The figures given for the following three years are approximate.

	Quan. Minted	Very Fine	Proof
1836. Obv. as above with C. Gobrecht in field between base and date. Rev. Eagle flying left amid stars. Plain edge. (Rare.)...........18			$ 900.00
1836. Obv. as above. Rev. Eagle flying in plain field. Plain edge. (Very rare.)................5			1000.00
1836. C. Gobrecht on base. Rev. Eagle flying left in field containing stars. Plain edge. Although scarce, this is the most common variety...........................1,000		$275.00	675 00
1836. As above, reeded edge. (Very rare.).............3			1400.00
1838. Seated Liberty. Obv. name of designer is left off and stars added around obverse border. Rev. Eagle flying left surrounded by stars. Reeded edge. (Rare.).........25			1500.00
1838. As above, plain edge. (Very rare.)..............3			1700.00
1838. Obv. as above. Rev. Eagle in plain field. Plain edge. (Very rare.).....................3			1700.00
1839. Obv. same as 1838. Rev. Eagle in plain field. Plain edge. (Very rare.)................3			1700.00
1839. Obv. as above. Rev. Eagle amid stars. Plain edge. (Very rare.)....................3			1700.00
1839. Obv. as above. Rev. Eagle in plain field. Reeded edge. Most common 1839 variety. (Rare.)..............................300		300.00	900.00

SILVER DOLLARS
U. S. SILVER DOLLARS — Regular Issues

Fine — All drapery lines show but partly worn. Hair from brow, over ear and down neck, well outlined but shows only slight detail.

V. Fine — LIBERTY is strong and its ribbon shows slight wear.

	Quan. Minted	Fine	V. Fine
1840	61,005	$10.00	$21.00
1841	173,000	7.00	13.50
1842	184,618	6.00	12.00
1843	165,100	6.00	12.00
1844	20,000	10.00	21.00
1845	24,500	10.00	21.00
1846	110,600	6.00	12.00
1846O	59,000	9.00	18.00
1847	140,750	6.00	12.00
1848	15,000	13.50	27.00
1849	62,600	7.50	15.00
1850	7,500	22.50	45.00
1850O	40,000	10.00	21.00
		V. Fine	Proof
1851 (Original)	1,300	350.00	900.00
			Unc.
1852 (Original)	1,100	325.00	900.00
		Fine	V. Fine
1853	46,110	15.00	30.00
1854	33,140	30.00	57.50
1855	26,000	26.00	51.00
1856	63,500	15.00	30.00
1857	94,000	17.00	33.00
1858 (Not mentioned in Director's report)	80	Proof	1000.00
1859	256,500	9.00	18.00
1859O	360,000	6.00	12.00
1859S	20,000	15.00	30.00
1860	218,930	9.00	18.00
1860O	515,000	6.00	12.00
1861	78,500	12.50	24.00
1862	12,090	11.50	22.50
1863	27,660	11.50	22.50
1864	31,170	11.50	22.50
1865	47,000	11.50	22.50

SILVER DOLLARS

	Quan. Minted	Fine	V. Fine
1866 (First year with motto.)	49,625	$ 10.00	$ 21.00
"In God We Trust"			
1867	60,325	10.00	21.00
1868	182,700	10.00	21.00
1869	424,300	5.50	11.25
1870	433,000	5.50	11.00
1870CC	12,462	22.50	45.00
1870S (No mention in Treasurer's report.)		4,000.00	6,500.00
1871	1,115,760	5.00	9.75
1871CC	1,376	200.00	390.00
1872	1,106,450	5.00	9.75
1872CC	3,150	100.00	195.00
1872S	9,000	25.00	48.00
1873	293,600	6.00	11.50
1873CC	2,300	245.00	480 00
1873S (Unknown)	700		

George T. Morgan designed the silver dollar which was first issued in 1878 and because of the similarity of design the dimes, quarters and halves of that period were credited to him also. Strangely enough the Liberty Head dollar is generally known as the "Bland" dollar after Richard P. Bland, co-author of the Bland Silver Bill of 1878 which provided for the new design.

Ex. Fine — All hairlines strong and ear bold. Eagle's feathers all plain but slight wear on breast and wing tips.

SILVER DOLLARS

	Quan. Minted	Ex. Fine	Unc.
1878 All kinds	10,509,550		
7 tail feathers		$ 1.00	$ 1.50
8 tail feathers		2.00	3.00
1878CC	2,212,000	1.25	3.25
1878S	9,774,000	1.00	1.40
1879	14,807,100	1.00	1.25
1879CC	756,000	10.00	45.00
1879O	2,887,000	1.25	4.00

(12 in proof. New Orleans mint
resumed operations 2-20-1879.)

	Quan. Minted	Ex. Fine	Unc.
1879S	9,110,000	1.00	1.25
1880	12,601,355	1.00	1.25
1880CC	591,000	3.50	10.00
1880O	5,305,000	1.25	2.50
1880S	8,900,000	1.00	1.25
1881	9,163,975	1.00	1.25
1881CC	296,000	3.50	10.00
1881O	5,708,000	1.00	1.50
1881S	12,760,000	1.00	1.35
1882	11,101,100	1.00	1.25
1882CC	1,133,000	2.00	5.00
1882O	6,090,000	1.25	2.25
1882S	9,250,000	1.00	1.25
1883	12,291,039	1.00	1.25
1883CC	1,204,000	2.25	6.00
1883O	8,725,000	1.00	1.75
1883S	6,250,000	1.75	4.50
1884	14,070,875	1.00	1.25
1884CC	1,136,000	2.75	8.00
1884O	9,730,000	1.00	1.85
1884S	3,200,000	2.00	7.75
1885	17,787,767	1.00	1.25
1885CC	228,000	3.00	10.00
1885O	9,185,000	1.00	1.35
1885S	1,497,000	2.00	4.50
1886	19,963,886	1.00	1.25
1886O	10,710,000	1.00	2.00
1886S	750,000	2.00	9.50
1887	20,290,710	1.00	1.25
1887O	11,550,000	1.00	2.50
1887S	1,771,000	2.00	5.50
1888	19,183,833	1.00	1.25
1888O	12,150,000	1.00	2.25
1888S	657,000	1.50	10.00
1889	21,726,811	1.00	1.25
1889CC	350,000	50.00	150.00
1889O	11,875,000	1.00	4.00
1889S	700,000	1.00	9.00
1890	16,802,590	1.00	1.25
1890CC	2,309,041	1.50	4.50
1890O	10,701,000	1.00	3.00
1890S	8,230,373	1.00	1.75
1891	8,694,206	1.00	1.25

SILVER DOLLARS

	Quan. Minted	Ex. Fine	Unc.
1891CC	1,618,000	$ 1.50	$ 4.50
1891O	7,954,529	1.25	4.00
1891S	5,296,000	1.00	1.75
1892	1,037,245	1.50	4.75
1892CC	1,352,000	4.50	14.00
1892O	2,744,000	2.00	9.00
1892S	1,200,000	10.00	90.00
1893	378,792	2.00	6.50
1893CC	677,000	6.00	32.50
1893O	300,000	2.25	22.50
1893S	100,000	50.00	500.00
1894	110,972	7.50	30.00
1894O	1,723,000	2.00	6.50
1894S	1,260,000	3.00	10.00

			Proof
1895 Beware — Removed mint mark	12,880	500.00	1100.00

			Unc.
1895O	450,000	7.00	30.00
1895S	400,000	12.50	60.00
1896	9,976,762	1.00	1.35
1896O	4,900,000	1.50	6.50
1896S	5,000,000	3.50	30.00
1897	2,822,731	1.00	1.25
1897O	4,004,000	1.50	5.50
1897S	5,825,000	1.25	2.75
1898	5,884,735	1.00	2.00
1898O	4,440,000	1.00	2.50
1898S	4,102,000	2.00	6.50
1899	330,846	1.75	6.00
1899O	12,290,000	1.00	1.50
1899S	2,562,000	1.75	6.50
1900	8,830,912	1.00	1.25
1900O	12,590,000	1.00	1.50
1900S	3,540,000	1.50	6.50
1901	6,962,813	3.00	17.50
1901O	13,320,000	1.00	1.50
1901S	2,284,000	2.00	10.00
1902	7,994,777	1.00	1.25
1902O	8,636,000	1.00	1.50
1902S	1,530,000	2.75	11.00
1903	4,652,755	1.00	1.35
1903O	4,450,000	2.00	8.00
1903S	1,241,000	3.50	35.00
1904	2,788,650	1.50	4.00
1904O	3,720,000	1.00	1.50
1904S	2,304,000	1.50	22.50
1921 Morgan type	44,690,000	1.00	1.00
1921D Morgan type	20,345,000	1.00	1.00
1921S Morgan type	21,695,000	1.00	1.00

270,232,722 silver dollars were melted under the Pittman Act of April, 1918. 259,121,554 for export to India, and 11,111,168 for domestic subsidiary coins, which probably accounts for the scarcity of some dates.

SILVER DOLLARS

Agitation for the Peace Dollar started during the 1920 American Numismatic Association convention in Chicago. A special committee petitioned government authorities to produce a commemorative peace coin. A half-dollar was under consideration for a time, but the silver dollar afforded a better opportunity for art effect than a smaller coin. The new coin was authorized without congressional action, under the terms of the Pittman Act, which referred to the bullion and in no way affected the design.

Anthony de Francisci designed the new dollar, which was placed in circulation January 3, 1922.

Ex. Fine — Hairlines over brow and ear are strong though slightly worn. Outside wing feathers at right and those at top are visible but faint.

	Quan. Minted	Ex. Fine	Unc.
1921 Peace type	1,006,473	$ 4.00	$10.00
1922	51,737,000	1.00	1.00
1922D	15,063,000	1.00	1.25
1922S	17,475,000	1.00	2.00
1923	30,800,000	1.00	1.10
1923D	6,811,000	1.00	3.00
1923S	19,020,000	1.00	3.00
1924	11,811,000	1.00	1.10
1924S	1,728,000	1.00	4.00
1925	10,198,000	1.00	1.10
1925S	1,610,000	1.00	3.00
1926	1,939,000	1.00	1.25
1926D	2,348,700	1.50	6.00
1926S	6,980,000	1.00	3.00
1927	848,000	1.50	9.00
1927D	1,268,900	1.50	7.50
1927S	866,000	1.50	10.00
1928	360,649	10.00	25.00
1928S	1,632,000	2.00	9.00
1934	954,057	2.75	3.50
1934D	1,569,500	2.00	4.50
1934S	1,011,000	5.50	80.00
1935	1,576,000	1.50	3.50
1935S	1,964,000	2.25	8.00

TRADE DOLLARS
(Coined from 1873 to 1885)

This coin was issued for circulation in the Orient to compete with the Mexican peso. When first coined they were legal tender in United States to the extent of $5.00 but with the decline in price of silver bullion Congress repealed the legal tender provision in 1876 and authorized the Treasury to limit coinage to export demand. In 1887 a law was passed authorizing the Treasury to redeem all Trade dollars which were not mutilated. U.S. Trade dollars are no longer circulating in the Orient. Those struck in the last few years of coinage were undoubtedly all proofs to satisfy collectors' demands.

Fine — *Mottoes and LIBERTY readable but worn.*
Ex. Fine — *Mottoes and LIBERTY are sharp. Only slight wear on rims.*

	Quan. Minted	Fine	Ex. Fine
1873	397,500	$ 9.00	$12.50
1873CC	124,500	12.50	25.00
1873S	703,000	9.00	20.00
1874	987,800	5.50	9.50
1874CC	1,373,200	10.00	20.00
1874S	2,549,000	5.00	8.00
1875	218,900	6.50	11.00
1875CC	1,573,700	9.00	16.00
1875S	4,487,000	5.00	8.00
1876	456,150	5.00	8.00
1876CC	509,000	8.50	17.50
1876S	5,227,000	5.00	7.50
1877	3,039,710	5.00	6.50
1877CC	534,000	16.00	35.00
1877S	9,519,000	4.50	6.50
1878	900	Proof	55.00
1878CC	97,000	45.00	80.00
1878S	4,162,000	4.50	6.50
			Proof
1879	1,541		42.50
1880	1,987		42.50
1881	960		47.50
1882	1,097		45.00
1883	979		60.00
1884	10		5,000.00
1885	5		7,500.00

The trade dollars of 1884 and 1885 were unknown to collectors generally until 1908. None is listed in the Director's report. The law authorizing Trade Dollars was repealed in February, 1887.

GOLD DOLLARS

Coinage of the gold dollar was begun in 1849; those coined 1849 to 1854 are known as the Liberty head or small sized type. In 1854 the piece was made larger in diameter and thinner and the design was changed to a feather headdress on a female, popularly known as the Indian head type or large size gold dollar (1854 was coined in both types). In 1856 the type was changed slightly by enlarging the size of the head.

Prices for gold given in this handbook are for coins in "fine" or better condition only. Dealers do not purchase gold coins on a bullion basis, therefore there is no numismatic market for gold in less than fine condition.

Fine — Full LIBERTY on headband. All hairlines and beads worn smooth.

Ex. Fine — Little wear on hair, knobs on coronet must be bold.

	Quan. Minted	Fine	Ex. Fine
1849	688,567	$20.00	$25.00
1849C	11,634	35.00	50.00
1849D	21,588	35.00	50.00
1849O	215,000	21.00	25.00
1850	481,953	19.00	25.00
1850C	6,965	65.00	80.00
1850D	8,382	65.00	80.00
1850O	14,000	21.00	23.00
1851	3,317,671	18.00	23.00
1851C	41,267	35.00	60.00
1851D	9,882	35.00	60.00
1851O	290,000	20.00	23.00
1852	2,045,351	19.00	23.00
1852C	9,434	50.00	60.00
1852D	6,360	50.00	60.00
1852O	140,000	18.00	23.00
1853	4,076,051	18.00	23.00
1853C	11,515	35.00	55.00
1853D	6,583	60.00	80.00
1853O	290,000	18.00	25.00
1854 (Total Coinage — Lg. and Sm.)	1,639,445	18.00	25.00
1854D	2,935	90.00	110.00
1854S	14,632	25.00	35.00

Fine — Tips of feather curls on headdress partially worn away.

Ex. Fine — Slight wear on headdress feather curls.

1854		40.00	60.00
1855	758,269	40.00	60.00
1855C	9,803	60.00	90.00
1855D	1,811	250.00	400.00
1855O	55,000	50.00	45.00
1856S	24,600	50.00	70.00

GOLD DOLLARS

Fine — Full LIBERTY in headband. Beads partially worn. Curled feathers worn flat.
Ex. Fine — Trace of wear above and right of eye and on curled feathers.

	Quan. Minted	Fine	Ex. Fine
1856	1,762,936	$20.00	$25.00
1856D	1,460	300.00	350.00
1857	774,789	20.00	25.00
1857C	13,280	42.50	65.00
1857D	3,533	100.00	150.00
1857S	10,000	30.00	42.50
1858	117,995	20.00	25.00
1858D	3,477	75.00	125.00
1858S	10,000	35.00	42.50
1859	168,244	20.00	25.00
1859C	5,235	62.50	85.00
1859D	4,952	67.50	110.00
1859S	15,000	30.00	50.00
1860	36,668	21.00	25.00
1860D	1,566	400.00	600.00
1860S	13,000	30.00	50.00
1861	527,499	21.00	25.00
1861D		1000.00	1500.00
1862	1,326,865	21.00	26.00
1863	6,250	60.00	85.00
1864	5,950	35.00	45.00
1865	3,725	60.00	70.00
1866	7,180	37.50	45.00
1867	5,250	30.00	35.00
1868	10,525	22.00	26.00
1869	5,925	30.00	37.50
1870	6,335	30.00	37.50
1870S	3,000	115.00	185.00
1871	3,930	22.00	30.00
1872	3,530	23.00	30.00
1873	125,125	20.00	26.00
1874	198,820	20.00	26.00
1875	420	175.00	250.00
1876	3,245	22.00	27.50
1877	3,920	22.00	27.50
1878	3,020	22.00	27.50
1879	3,030	22.00	27.50
1880	1,636	32.50	42.50
1881	7,660	22.00	27.50
1882	5,040	22.00	27.50
1883	10,840	22.00	27.50
1884	6,206	22.00	27.50
1885	12,205	22.00	27.50
1886	6,016	22.00	27.50
1887	8,543	22.00	27.50
1888	16,080	22.00	27.50
1889	30,729	22.00	27.50

QUARTER EAGLES ($2.50 Gold Pieces)

Coinage began in 1796 and the last year is dated 1929. Most of the dates prior to 1834 are rare, some excessively rare; after 1834 only scattered dates are considered rare. One of these, 1848, has the letters CAL over the eagle in reference to California gold.

Fine — Hair worn smooth on high spots. E. PLURIBUS UNUM weak but readable.

Ex. Fine — Slight wear on high spots.

	Quan. Minted	Fine	Ex. Fine
1796 No Stars	897	$800.00	$2100.00

	Quan. Minted	Fine	Ex. Fine
1796 With Stars	66	700.00	2000.00
1797	1,756	400.00	1000.00
1798	614	500.00	1000.00
1802 Over 1	2,612	200.00	900.00
1804	3,327	225.00	750.00
1805	1,781	225.00	750.00
1806 Over 4 - All kinds	1,616	250.00	1000.00
1806 Over 5		250.00	600.00
1807	6,812	175.00	500.00

Fine — E. PLURIBUS UNUM and LIBERTY on headband readable but weak.

Ex. Fine — Motto and LIBERTY sharp. Liberty's hair only slightly worn.

	Quan. Minted	Fine	Ex. Fine
1808	2,710	750.00	2450.00
1821 Reduced Size	6,448	135.00	325.00
1824 Over 21	2,600	100.00	300.00
1825	4,434	100.00	300.00
1826 Over 25	760	200.00	550.00
1827	2,800	135.00	225.00
1829	3,403	125.00	450.00
1830	4,540	125.00	450.00
1831	4,520	125.00	450.00
1832	4,400	125.00	450.00
1833	4,160	125.00	450.00
1834 With motto over the eagle	4,000	250.00	450.00

QUARTER EAGLES ($2.50 Gold Pieces)

Fine — LIBERTY readable and complete. Curl under ear outlined but no detail.
Ex. Fine — Slight wear on hair at top of head, below "L" in LIBERTY, top of coronet and on reverse, upper wings and neck of eagle.

	Quan. Minted	Fine	Ex. Fine
1834 Without motto	112,234	$17.00	$27.00
1835	131,402	17.00	27.00
1836	547,986	17.00	27.00
1837	45,080	17.00	27.00
1838	47,030	17.00	27.00
1838C	7,908	50.00	80.00
1839	27,021	17.00	27.00
1839C	18,173	47.50	60.00
1839D	13,674	50.00	77.50
1839O	17,781	35.00	50.00

1840	18,859	17.00	27.00
1840C	12,838	30.00	55.00
1840D	3,532	50.00	75.00
1840O	26,200	20.00	32.50
1841 (Proofs only) Beware — Removed mint mark		Proof	2500.00
1841C	10,297	40.00	55.00
1841D	4,164	50.00	75.00
1842	2,823	35.00	50.00
1842C	6,737	40.00	55.00
1842D	4,643	40.00	55.00
1842O	19,800	18.00	30.00
1843	100,546	17.00	27.00
1843C Large or small date	26,096	35.00	50.00
1843D Small date	36,209	35.00	50.00
1843O Large date		20.00	30.00
1843O Small date	368,002	18.00	28.00
1844	6,784	30.00	45.00
1844C	11,622	35.00	50.00
1844D	17,332	35.00	50.00
1845	91,051	20.00	30.00
1845D	19,460	35.00	47.50
1845O		40.00	60.00
1846	21,598	20.00	30.00
1846C	4,808	40.00	70.00
1846D	19,303	32.50	60.00
1846O	66,000	20.00	30.00
1847	29,814	20.00	30.00
1847C	23,226	30.00	45.00
1847D	15,784	35.00	50.00
1847O	124,000	20.00	32.50
1848	7,497	75.00	125.00

QUARTER EAGLES ($2.50 Gold Pieces)

CAL above eagle on Reverse

CALIF. GOLD QUARTER EAGLE

In 1848 about two hundred and thirty ounces of gold were sent to Secretary of War Marcy by Col. R. B. Mason, Military governor of California. The gold was turned over to the mint and made into quarter eagles. The distinguishing mark "CAL" was punched above the eagle on the reverse side, while the coins were in the die.

	Quan. Minted	Fine	Ex. Fine
1848 CAL over eagle	1,389	$1000.00	$1500.00
1848C	16,788	35.00	50.00
1848D	13,771	35.00	55.00
1849	23,294	20.00	32.50
1849C	10,220	40.00	57.50
1849D	10,945	40.00	57.50
1850	252,923	20.00	32.50
1850C	9,148	42.50	55.00
1850D	12,148	40.00	52.50
1850O	84,000	20.00	30.00
1851	1,372,748	20.00	27.00
1851C	14,923	40.00	60.00
1851D	11,264	40.00	60.00
1851O	148,000	20.00	27.00
1852	1,159,681	20.00	27.00
1852C	9,772	42.50	75.00
1852D	4,078	60.00	100.00
1852O	140,000	20.00	27.00
1853	1,404,668	20.00	27.00
1853D	3,178	90.00	120.00
1854	596,258	20.00	27.00
1854C	7,295	50.00	90.00
1854D	1,760	240.00	375.00
1854O	153,000	20.00	27.00
1854S	246	850.00	1250.00
1855	235,480	20.00	27.00
1855C	3,677	60.00	85.00
1855D	1,123	210.00	340.00
1856	384,240	20.00	27.00
1856C	7,913	50.00	75.00
1856D	874	300.00	450.00
1856O	21,100	20.00	27.00
1856S	71,120	21.00	29.00
1857	214,130	20.00	27.00
1857D	2,364	60.00	85.00
1857O	34,000	20.00	27.00
1857S	68,000	21.00	28.00
1858	47,377	20.00	27.00
1858C	9,056	50.00	75.00
1859	39,444	20.00	27.00

QUARTER EAGLES ($2.50 Gold Pieces)

	Quan. Minted	Fine	Ex. Fine
1859D	2,244	$60.00	$90.00
1859S	15,200	21.00	29.00
1860	22,675	20.00	27.00
1860C	7,469	45.00	70.00
1860S	35,600	20.00	27.00
1861	1,272,518	20.00	27.00
1861S	24,000	20.00	27.00
1862	112,353	20.00	27.00
1862S	8,000	25.00	37.50
1863 (Proofs only) Beware — Removed mint mark	30	Proof	1100.00
1863S	10,800	25.00	40.00
1864	2,874	70.00	95.00
1865	1,545	75.00	100.00
1865S	23,376	20.00	27.00
1866	3,110	60.00	90.00
1866S	38,960	17.50	29.00
1867	3,250	30.00	42.50
1867S	28,000	22.50	35.00
1868	3,625	32.50	60.00
1868S	34,000	20.00	29.00
1869	4,345	27.50	37.50
1869S	29,500	20.00	28.00
1870	4,555	27.50	40.00
1870S	16,000	20.00	28.00
1871	5,350	25.00	40.00
1871S	22,000	20.00	29.00
1872	3,030	22.00	34.50
1872S	18,000	21.00	32.50
1873	178,025	20.00	27.00
1873S	27,000	20.00	27.00
1874	3,940	25.00	40.00
1875	420	150.00	210.00
1875S	11,600	24.00	35.00
1876	4,221	25.00	40.00
1876S	5,000	20.00	29.00
1877	1,652	40.00	65.00
1877S	35,400	20.00	29.00
1878	286,260	20.00	29.00
1878S	178,000	20.00	29.00
1879	88,900	20.00	29.00
1879S	43,500	20.00	29.00
1880	2,996	35.00	50.00
1881	680	95.00	125.00
1882	4,040	30.00	50.00
1883	1,960	35.00	55.00
1884	1,993	35.00	55.00
1885	887	80.00	120.00
1886	4,088	26.00	37.50
1887	6,282	25.00	35.00
1888	16,098	20.00	28.00
1889	17,648	20.00	28.00
1890	8,813	25.00	35.00
1891	11,040	20.00	29.00

QUARTER EAGLES ($2.50 Gold Pieces)

	Quan. Minted	Fine	Ex. Fine
1892	2,545	$ 35.00	$ 50.00
1893	30,106	20.00	28.00
1894	4,122	22.00	30.00
1895	6,119	20.00	28.00
1896	19,202	20.00	27.00
1897	29,904	20.00	27.00
1898	24,165	20.00	27.00
1899	27,350	20.00	27.00
1900	67,205	20.00	27.00
1901	91,323	20.00	27.00
1902	133,733	20.00	27.00
1903	201,257	20.00	27.00
1904	160,960	20.00	27.00
1905	217,944	20.00	27.00
1906	176,490	20.00	27.00
1907	336,448	20.00	27.00

Fine — *Knot in hair cord shows, but top feathers faint on wing.*

Ex. Fine — *Cheek bone slightly worn. War-bonnet and headband feathers slightly worn.*

1908	565,057	12.00	17.00
1909	441,899	12.00	17.00
1910	492,682	12.00	17.00
1911	704,191	12.00	17.00
1911D	55,680	125.00	200.00
1912	616,197	12.00	17.00
1913	722,165	12.00	17.00
1914	240,117	17.50	25.00
1914D	448,000	13.50	18.50
1915	606,100	12.00	17.00
1925D	578,000	12.00	17.00
1926	446,000	12.00	17.00
1927	388,000	12.00	17.00
1928	416,000	12.00	17.00
1929	532,000	12.00	17.00

THREE-DOLLAR GOLD PIECES

(Coined from 1854 to 1889)

Authorized to facilitate postal transactions when the letter rate was made 3-cents. The coin was very unpopular and was never circulated to any extent; and when the postal rate was changed from 3-cents the piece was discontinued.

All dates are of the same design; those struck in 1873, 1875 and 1876 are the rarest. Only 20 specimens were coined of the 1875 in proof condition. Mint records state that 25 pieces were coined of 1873, but more are known to exist; in fact they do not bring as much money as the 1876 of which 45 were reported coined.

THREE-DOLLAR GOLD PIECES

Fine — Details of curled feathers missing. Beads partly worn, but LIBERTY plain.

Ex. Fine — Slight wear above and to right of eye, and tops of curled feathers.

	Quan. Minted	Fine	Ex. Fine
1854	138,618	$ 90.00	$140.00
1854D	1,120	425.00	750.00
1854O	24,000	90.00	140.00
1855	50,555	87.50	140.00
1855S	6,600	90.00	140.00
1856	26,010	87.50	140.00
1856S	34,500	90.00	140.00
1857	20,891	90.00	140.00
1857S	14,000	100.00	150.00
1858	2,133	90.00	150.00
1859	15,638	90.00	140.00
1860	7,155	95.00	150.00
1860S	7,000	100.00	160.00
1861	6,072	100.00	160.00
1862	5,785	100.00	160.00
1863	5,039	100.00	160.00
1864	2,680	110.00	175.00
1865	1,165	140.00	200.00
1866	4,030	110.00	150.00
1867	2,650	110.00	150.00
1868	4,875	110.00	150.00
1869	2,525	110.00	150.00
1870	3,535	110.00	150.00
1870S (Only 2 struck)			
1871	1,330	120.00	165.00
1872	2,030	110.00	150.00
1873 (Proofs only)	25	Proof	1,000.00
1874	41,820	90.00	140.00
1875 (Proofs only)	20	Proof	7,500.00
1876 (Proofs only)	45	Proof	2,500.00
1877	1,488	120.00	185.00
1878	82,324	90.00	145.00
1879	3,030	100.00	150.00
1880	1,036	110.00	175.00
1881	550	200.00	300.00
1882	1,540	110.00	175.00
1883	940	125.00	190.00
1884	1,106	125.00	190.00
1885	910	125.00	190.00
1886	1,142	110.00	175.00
1887	6,160	100.00	150.00
1888	5,291	100.00	150.00
1889	2,429	100.00	150.00

$4.00 GOLD OR "STELLA"

Though a pattern coin, this is one of our most popular gold pieces.

This piece was first suggested by the Hon. John A. Kasson, then U.S. Minister to Austria, and it was through the efforts of Dr. W. W. Hubbell who patented the Goloid metal, used in making the Goloid Metric Dollars, that we have these beautiful and interesting pieces.

There are two distinct types of these patterns, issued only two years, known as Barber and Morgan designs. The Barber design has flowing hair and is much more common. The Morgan design has coiled hair and is excessively rare. Both very beautiful and artistic, obverse designs.

These pieces were struck in Gold, Aluminum, Copper, and White Metal. We list only those struck in Gold below.

	Quan. Minted	Proof
1879 Flowing hair, Proof	415	$ 4,000.00
1879 Coiled hair, Proof	10	9,000.00
1880 Flowing hair, Proof	15	9,000.00
1880 Coiled hair, Proof	10	11,000.00

HALF EAGLES ($5.00 Gold Pieces)
(Coined from 1795 to 1929)

Dates prior to 1807 do not bear any mark of value. 1795 to 1798 are rare; 1799 to 1814 are fairly plentiful; and those in the 1820's are all very rare and with the possible exception of 1820, 1823 and 1826, few collectors have ever owned a half eagle of that decade. The 1822 is considered the most valuable regular issue coin of the entire United States series, there being only three specimens known and one of these is in the U.S. mint collection and therefore not available to collectors.

Fine — Hair worn smooth but with distinct outline. After 1797 E. PLURIBUS UNUM is faint but readable.

Ex. Fine — Slight wear on hair and cheek.

	Small Eagle		Large Eagle	
	Quan. Minted		Fine	Ex. Fine
1795 Small eagle			$250.00	$450.00
1795 Large eagle (8,707 coined in 1795)			400.00	700.00
1796	3,399		250.00	450.00
1797 Small eagle			400.00	650.00

HALF EAGLES ($5.00 Gold Pieces)

	Quan. Minted	Fine	Ex. Fine
1797 Large eagle (6,406 coined in 1797)		$400.00	$600.00
1798 Small eagle			
1798 Large eagle (24,867 coined in 1798)		100.00	135.00

1799	7,451	90.00	150.00
1800	11,622	90.00	150.00
1802 Over 1	53,176	90.00	150.00
1803 Over 2	33,506	90.00	150.00
1804	30,475	90.00	150.00
1805	33,183	90.00	150.00
1806	64,093	90.00	150.00
1807 Bust facing right	33,496	90.00	150.00

Fine — LIBERTY readable but partly weak.

Ex. Fine — Slight wear on high points of hair and curls.

1807 Bust facing left	50,597	90.00	150.00
1808	55,578	90.00	150.00
1809	33,875	90.00	150.00
1810	100,287	90.00	150.00
1811	99,581	90.00	150.00
1812	58,087	90.00	150.00

1813	95,428	100.00	150.00
1814	15,454	100.00	150.00
1815	635	2,000.00	3,000.00
1818	48,588	100.00	160.00
1819	51,723	900.00	1,500.00

HALF EAGLES ($5.00 Gold Pieces)

	Quan. Minted	Fine	Ex. Fine
1820	263,806	$140.00	$250.00
1821	34,641	325.00	600.00
1822	17,796		———
1823	14,485	125.00	200.00
1824	17,340	450.00	750.00
1825	29,060	400.00	650.00
1826	18,069	400.00	800.00
1827	24,913	1,200.00	2,300.00
1828	28,029	700.00	1,100.00
1829	57,442	2,500.00	4,500.00
1830	126,351	200.00	325.00
1831	140,594	200.00	350.00
1832	157,487	550.00	1,000.00
1833	193,630	225.00	350.00
1834 Motto	50,141	250.00	400.00

1834 No motto. Plain 4	———	20.00	28.00
1834 No motto. Crosslet 4	682,028	60.00	135.00
1835	371,534	20.00	30.00
1836	553,147	20.00	30.00
1837	207,121	20.00	29.00
1838	286,588	20.00	29.00
1838C	12,913	50.00	75.00
1838D	20,583	50.00	75.00

Fine — LIBERTY readable, but partly weak. Neck hair worn, but outlines clear.

Ex. Fine — Hair at neck sharp. Slight wear top of coronet and hair beneath.

1839	118,143	20.00	29.00
1839C	23,467	40.00	65.00
1839D	18,939	40.00	65.00
1840	137,382	18.00	27.00
1840C	19,028	45.00	75.00
1840D	22,896	45.00	75.00
1840O	30,400	18.00	27.00
1841	15,833	18.00	27.00
1841C	21,511	35.00	50.00
1841D	30,495	35.00	50.00
1841O (2 Known)			———
1842	27,578	17.00	27.00

HALF EAGLES ($5.00 Gold Pieces)

	Quan. Minted	Fine	Ex. Fine
1842C	27,480	$ 45.00	$ 60.00
1842D	59,608	45.00	60.00
1842O	16,400	20.00	32.50
1843	611,205	12.00	15.00
1843C	44,353	40.00	60.00
1843D	98,452	42.50	65.00
1843O	101,075	12.00	15.00
1844	340,330	12.00	15.00
1844C	23,631	37.50	60.00
1844D	88,982	37.50	60.00
1844O	364,600	12.00	15.00
1845	417,099	12.00	15.00
1845D	90,629	40.00	62.50
1845O	41,000	18.00	28.00
1846	395,942	12.00	15.00
1846C	12,995	45.00	70.00
1846D	80,294	40.00	65.00
1846O	58,000	16.00	27.00
1847	915,981	12.00	15.00
1847C	84,151	35.00	60.00
1847D	64,405	50.00	65.00
1847O	12,000	22.50	35.00
1848	260,775	12.00	15.00
1848C	64,472	50.00	70.00
1848D	47,465	40.00	60.00
1849	133,070	12.00	15.00
1849C	64,823	40.00	60.00
1849D	39,036	40.00	60.00
1850	64,491	12.00	15.00
1850C	63,591	40.00	60.00
1850D	43,950	40.00	60.00
1851	377,505	12.00	15.00
1851C	49,176	40.00	60.00
1851D	62,710	42.50	62.50
1851O	41,000	16.00	28.00
1852	573,901	12.00	15.00
1852C	72,574	35.00	47.50
1852D	91,452	35.00	47.50
1853	305,770	12.00	15.00
1853C	65,571	35.00	45.00
1853D	89,678	35.00	45.00
1854	160,675	12.00	15.00
1854C	39,291	40.00	60.00
1854D	56,413	40.00	60.00
1854O	46,000	15.00	27.00
1854S	268	1,500.00	2,500.00
1855	117,098	12.00	15.00
1855C	39,788	40.00	60.00
1855D	22,432	42.50	62.50
1855O	11,100	20.00	30.00
1855S	61,000	12.00	15.00
1856	197,990	12.00	15.00
1856C	28,457	40.00	60.00

HALF EAGLES ($5.00 Gold Pieces)

	Quan. Minted	Fine	Ex. Fine
1856D	19,786	$ 40.00	$ 47.50
1856O	10,000	30.00	40.00
1856S	105,100	12.00	15.00
1857	98,188	12.00	15.00
1857C	31,360	37.50	50.00
1857D	17,046	37.50	50.00
1857O	13,000	17.00	25.00
1857S	87,000	12.00	15.00
1858	15,136	26.00	30.00
1858C	38,856	40.00	52.50
1858D	15,362	42.50	55.00
1858S	18,600	15.00	25.00
1859	16,814	15.00	25.00
1859C	31,847	35.00	47.50
1859D	10,366	37.50	50.00
1859S	13,220	15.00	25.00
1860	19,825	15.00	25.00
1860C	14,813	40.00	57.50
1860D	14,635	40.00	57.50
1860S	21,200	15.00	26.00
1861	639,950	12.00	15.00
1861C	6,879	65.00	80.00
1861D	1,597	115.00	150.00
1861S	18,000	15.00	20.00
1862	4,465	20.00	27.50
1862S	9,500	16.00	28.00
1863	2,472	40.00	60.00
1863S	17,000	16.00	25.00
1864	4,220	30.00	47.50
1864S	3,888	35.00	45.00
1865	1,295	60.00	72.50
1865S	27,612	15.00	26.00
1866S No motto (all kinds)	43,920	20.00	29.00

Fine — *IN GOD WE TRUST worn but readable and complete.*

Ex. Fine — *Slight wear on hair at top of head, below "L" in LIBERTY, top of coronet, and on reverse, upper wings and neck of eagle.*

1866 Motto	6,720	15.00	26.00
1866S		15.00	26.00
1867	6,920	15.00	26.00
1867S	29,000	15.00	26.00
1868	5,725	15.00	28.00
1868S	52,000	15.00	22.50
1869	1,785	40.00	60.00
1869S	31,000	15.00	25.00
1870	4,035	20.00	28.00
1870CC	7,675	20.00	28.00
1870S	17,000	15.00	26.00

HALF EAGLES ($5.00 Gold Pieces)

	Quan. Minted	Fine	Ex. Fine
1871	3,230	$16.00	$25.00
1871CC	20,770	23.00	30.00
1871S	25,000	15.00	23.00
1872	1,690	30.00	40.00
1872CC	16,980	20.00	30.00
1872S	36,400	15.00	23.00
1873	112,505	12.00	15.00
1873CC	7,416	25.00	35.00
1873S	31,000	15.00	24.00
1874	3,508	25.00	35.00
1874CC	21,198	20.00	27.50
1874S	16,000	15.00	20.00
1875	220	225.00	425.00
1875CC	11,828	20.00	27.50
1875S	9,000	15.00	20.00
1876	1,477	30.00	40.00
1876CC	6,887	20.00	27.50
1876S	4,000	16.00	26.00
1877	1,152	50.00	70.00
1877CC	8,680	25.00	35.00
1877S	26,700	16.00	24.00
1878	131,740	12.00	15.00
1878CC	9,054	20.00	27.50
1878S	144,700	12.00	15.00
1879	301,950	12.00	15.00
1879CC	17,281	20.00	30.00
1879S	426,200	12.00	15.00
1880	3,166,436	12.00	15.00
1880CC	51,017	18.00	26.00
1880S	1,348,900	12.00	15.00
1881	5,708,800	12.00	15.00
1881CC	13,886	15.00	28.00
1881S	969,000	12.00	15.00
1882	2,514,560	12.00	15.00
1882CC	82,817	17.00	25.00
1882S	969,999	12.00	15.00
1883	233,440	12.00	15.00
1883CC	12,958	20.00	27.50
1883S	83,200	15.00	24.00
1884	191,048	12.00	15.00
1884CC	16,402	19.00	27.50
1884S	177,000	12.00	15.00
1885	601,506	12.00	15.00
1885S	1,211,500	12.00	15.00
1886	388,432	12.00	15.00
1886S	3,268,000	12.00	15.00
1887 (Proofs only) Beware — removed mint mark	87	Proof	900.00
1887S	1,912,000	12.00	15.00
1888	18,296	15.00	26.00
1888S	293,900	12.00	15.00
1889	7,565	50.00	70.00
1890	4,328	50.00	70.00
1890CC	53,800	18.00	27.50

HALF EAGLES ($5.00 Gold Pieces)

	Quan. Minted	Fine	Ex. Fine
1891	61,413	$15.00	$25.00
1891CC	208,000	17.00	26.00
1892	753,572	12.00	15.00
1892CC	82,968	18.00	23.00
1892O	10,000	20.00	30.00
1892S	298,400	15.00	25.00
1893	1,528,197	12.00	15.00
1893CC	60,000	17.50	25.00
1893O	110,000	15.00	25.00
1893S	224,000	12.00	15.00
1894	957,955	12.00	15.00
1894O	16,600	16.00	26.00
1894S	55,900	16.00	26.00
1895	1,345,936	12.00	15.00
1895S	112,000	12.00	15.00
1896	59,063	12.00	15.00
1896S	155,400	12.00	15.00
1897	867,883	12.00	15.00
1897S	354,000	12.00	15.00
1898	633,495	12.00	15.00
1898S	1,397,400	12.00	15.00
1899	1,710,729	12.00	15.00
1899S	1,545,000	12.00	15.00
1900	1,405,730	12.00	15.00
1900S	329,000	12.00	15.00
1901	616,040	12.00	15.00
1901S	3,648,000	12.00	15.00
1902	172,562	12.00	15.00
1902S	939,000	12.00	15.00
1903	227,024	12.00	15.00
1903S	1,855,000	12.00	15.00
1904	392,136	12.00	15.00
1904S	97,000	20.00	30.00
1905	302,308	12.00	15.00
1905S	880,700	12.00	15.00
1906	348,820	12.00	15.00
1906D	320,000	12.00	15.00
1906S	598,000	12.00	15.00
1907	626,192	12.00	15.00
1907D	888,000	12.00	15.00
1908 Liberty head	421,874	12.00	15.00

Prices shown
are for
well-struck
mint marks

Fine — Knot in hair cord shows, but top feathers faint on wing.
Ex. Fine — Slight wear on cheekbone and jawbone beneath. Top feathers on wing outlined but worn.

1908 Indian head	578,012	11.00	14.50
1908D	148,000	11.00	14.50

HALF EAGLES ($5.00 Gold Pieces)

		Quan. Minted	Fine	Ex. Fine
1908S		82,000	$ 25.00	$ 40.00
1909		627,138	13.00	18.00
1909D		3,423,560	12.00	14.50
1909O (Beware of Spurious O Mint Mark)		34,200	110.00	150.00
1909S		297,200	15.00	19.00
1910		604,250	11.00	14.50
1910D		193,600	11.00	14.50
1910S		770,200	14.00	18.00
1911		915,139	11.00	14.50
1911D		72,500	30.00	70.00
1911S		1,416,000	13.00	18.00
1912	Prices shown	790,144	11.00	14.50
1912S	are for	392,000	13.00	18.00
1913	well-struck	916,099	11.00	14.50
1913S	mint marks	408,000	16.00	21.00
1914		247,125	11.00	14.50
1914D		247,000	12.00	15.50
1914S		263,000	12.00	18.50
1915		588,075	11.00	14.50
1915S		164,000	14.00	18.00
1916S		240,000	14.00	18.00
1929		662,000	200.00	450.00

EAGLES ($10.00 Gold Pieces)

(Coined from 1795 to 1933; none coined between 1805 and 1837)

Although coinage extended over a long period there are really only three major types with some minor variations such as the number of stars in the first type; the liberty head was adopted in 1838 and coined until 1907, a motto being added on the reverse in 1866; the Indian head type was introduced in 1907. The rarest date Eagle is 1798.

Fine — Details on turban and head obliterated.

Ex. Fine — Noticeable wear points are: hair left of eye, strand which sweeps across turban and eagle's wingtips.

		Fine	Ex. Fine
1795	2,795	375.00	500.00
1796	6,080	325.00	475.00
1797 Small eagle (9,177 coined in 1797)		300.00	450.00

EAGLES ($10.00 Gold Pieces)

	Quan. Minted	Fine	Ex. Fine
1797 Large eagle...............................		$225.00	$300.00
1798 Over 97. 4 stars facing (7,974 coined in 1798).......		500.00	700.00
1798 Over 97. 6 stars facing........................		1,300.00	1,750.00
1799..	17,483	200.00	250.00
1800..	25,965	175.00	225.00
1801..	29,254	170.00	220.00
1803..	8,979	175.00	225.00
1804..	9,795	200.00	300.00

Fine — LIBERTY readable but may be slightly worn.

Ex. Fine — Wear shows at top of head, hair below "L" in LIBERTY, top of coronet, upper part of wings and neck of eagle.

	Quan. Minted	Fine	Ex. Fine
1838..	7,200	142.50	200.00
1839..	38,248	70.00	90.00
1840..	47,338	22.00	30.00
1841..	63,131	22.00	30.00
1841O...	2,500	50.00	70.00
1842..	81,507	22.00	30.00
1842O...	27,400	22.00	30.00
1843..	75,462	22.00	30.00
1843O...	175,162	22.00	30.00
1844..	6,361	30.00	50.00
1844O...	118,700	22.00	30.00
1845..	26,153	22.00	30.00
1845O...	47,500	22.00	30.00
1846..	20,095	22.00	30.00
1846O...	81,780	22.00	30.00
1847..	862,258	22.00	30.00
1847O...	571,500	22.00	30.00
1848..	145,484	22.00	30.00
1848O...	35,850	22.00	30.00
1849..	653,618	22.00	30.00
1849O...	23,900	22.00	30.00
1850..	291,451	22.00	30.00

EAGLES ($10.00 Gold Pieces)

		Quan. Minted	Fine	Ex. Fine
1850O		57,500	$ 22.00	$ 30.00
1851		176,328	22.00	30.00
1851O		263,000	22.00	30.00
1852		263,106	22.00	30.00
1852O		18,000	22.00	30.00
1853		201,253	22.00	30.00
1853O		51,000	22.00	30.00
1854		54,250	22.00	30.00
1854O		52,500	22.00	30.00
1854S		123,826	22.00	30.00
1855	Prices listed for all gold	121,701	22.00	30.00
1855O	coins are for choice speci-	18,000	22.00	30.00
1855S	mens. Those grading less	9,000	30.00	45.00
1856	than the condition listed	60,490	22.00	30.00
1856O	bring proportionately less.	14,500	23.00	32.00
1856S		68,000	22.00	30.00
1857		16,606	22.00	30.00
1857O		5,500	40.00	60.00
1857S		26,000	22.00	30.00
1858	(Beware — removed mint	2,521	1,500.00	2,500.00
1858O	mark.)	20,000	22.00	30.00
1858S		11,800	24.00	32.00
1859		16,093	24.00	30.00
1859O		2,300	65.00	90.00
1859S		7,000	35.00	45.00
1860		11,783	30.00	40.00
1860O		11,100	27.00	37.00
1860S		5,000	40.00	70.00
1861		113,233	22.00	30.00
1861S		15,500	24.00	32.00
1862		10,995	24.00	32.00
1862S		12,500	24.00	32.00
1863		1,248	60.00	95.00
1863S		10,000	27.00	32.00
1864		3,580	35.00	55.00
1864S		2,500	35.00	65.00
1865		4,005	37.00	50.00
1865S		16,700	22.00	30.00
1866S (Both Kinds)		20,000	37.00	47.00

Fine — *IN GOD WE TRUST worn but readable and complete.*

Ex. Fine — *Wear shows at top of head, hair below "L" in LIBERTY, top of coronet, upper part of wings and neck of eagle.*

1866	3,780	42.00	52.00
1866S		25.00	35.00
1867	3,140	29.00	37.00
1867S	9,000	27.00	33.00

EAGLES ($10.00 Gold Pieces)

	Quan. Minted	Fine	Ex. Fine
1868	10,655	$24.00	$30.00
1868S	13,500	24.00	30.00
1869	1,855	55.00	75.00
1869S	6,430	25.00	32.00
1870	2,535	35.00	47.00
1870CC	5,908	47.00	57.00
1870S	8,000	25.00	32.00
1871	1,780	50.00	85.00
1871CC	7,185	37.00	50.00
1871S	16,500	25.00	35.00
1872	1,650	50.00	75.00
1872CC	5,500	50.00	60.00
1872S	17,300	25.00	32.00
1873	825	90.00	150.00
1873CC	4,543	50.00	65.00
1873S	12,000	25.00	35.00
1874	53,160	17.50	21.00
1874CC	16,767	23.00	31.00
1874S	10,000	22.00	30.00
1875	120	300.00	400.00
1875CC	7,715	32.00	45.00
1876	732	100.00	200.00
1876CC	4,696	35.00	45.00
1876S	5,000	23.00	30.00
1877	817	100.00	200.00
1877CC	3,332	40.00	55.00
1877S	17,000	22.00	30.00
1878	73,800	17.50	21.00
1878CC	3,244	40.00	50.00
1878S	26,100	22.00	30.00
1879	384,770	17.50	21.00
1879CC	1,762	45.00	55.00
1879O	1,500	90.00	125.00
1879S	224,000	17.50	21.00
1880	1,644,876	17.50	21.00
1880CC	11,190	30.00	42.00
1880O	9,200	27.00	35.00
1880S	506,250	17.50	21.00
1881	3,877,260	17.50	21.00
1881CC	24,015	27.00	35.00
1881O	8,350	30.00	40.00
1881S	970,000	17.50	21.00
1882	2,324,480	17.50	21.00
1882CC	6,764	37.00	47.00
1882O	10,820	25.00	32.00
1882S	132,000	17.50	21.00
1883	208,740	22.00	28.00
1883CC	12,000	27.00	37.00
1883O	800	250.00	350.00
1883S	38,000	23.00	27.00
1884	76,905	17.50	21.00
1884CC	9,925	30.00	40.00
1884S	124,250	22.00	28.00
1885	253,527	17.50	21.00

EAGLES ($10.00 Gold Pieces)

	Quan. Minted	Fine	Ex. Fine
1885S	228,000	$17.50	$21.00
1886	236,160	17.50	21.00
1886S	826,000	17.50	21.00
1887	53,680	22.00	28.00
1887S	817,000	17.50	21.00
1888	132,996	17.50	21.00
1888O	21,335	27.00	35.00
1888S	648,700	17.50	21.00
1889	4,485	50.00	70.00
1889S	425,400	17.50	21.00
1890	58,043	22.00	28.00
1890CC	17,500	25.00	32.00
1891	91,868	17.50	21.00
1891CC	103,732	24.00	32.00
1892	797,552	17.50	21.00
1892CC	40,000	26.00	33.00
1892O	28,688	25.00	32.00
1892S	115,500	22.00	28.00
1893	1,840,895	17.50	21.00
1893CC	14,000	27.00	37.00
1893O	17,000	26.00	36.00
1893S	141,350	17.50	21.00
1894	2,470,778	17.50	21.00
1894O	107,500	22.00	28.00
1894S	25,000	22.00	28.00
1895	567,826	17.50	21.00
1895O	98,000	22.00	28.00
1895S	49,000	22.00	28.00
1896	76,348	17.50	21.00
1896S	123,750	17.50	21.00
1897	1,000,159	17.50	21.00
1897O	42,500	22.00	28.00
1897S	234,750	17.50	21.00
1898	812,197	17.50	21.00
1898S	473,600	17.50	21.00
1899	1,262,305	17.50	21.00
1899O	37,047	22.00	28.00
1899S	841,000	17.50	21.00
1900	293,960	17.50	21.00
1900S	81,000	17.50	21.00
1901	1,718,825	17.50	21.00
1901O	72,041	22.00	28.00
1901S	2,812,750	17.50	21.00
1902	82,513	22.00	28.00
1902S	469,500	17.50	21.00
1903	125,926	17.50	21.00
1903O	112,771	22.00	28.00
1903S	538,000	17.50	21.00
1904	162,038	22.00	28.00
1904O	108,950	22.00	28.00
1905	201,078	17.50	21.00
1905S	369,250	17.50	21.00
1906	165,497	17.50	21.00
1906D	981,000	17.50	21.00

EAGLES ($10.00 Gold Pieces)

	Quan. Minted	Fine	Ex. Fine
1906O	86,895	$ 22.00	$ 28.00
1906S	457,000	17.50	21.00
1907 Liberty head	1,203,973	17.50	21.00
1907D Liberty	1,030,000	17.50	21.00
1907S Liberty	210,500	17.50	21.00

Fine—Full LIBERTY. Feathers on bonnet noticeably worn. Eagles left wing, leaves at left of eagle's perch and talons show wear.

Ex. Fine — Trace of wear on cheek bone, feathers on headdress, above eagle's eye and left wing.

	Quan. Minted	Fine	Ex. Fine
1907 Indian, reg	239,406	22.00	28.00
1907 Indian, wire edge, periods	500	150.00	250.00
1907 Indian, rolled edge, periods	42	500.00	900.00
1908 No motto	33,500	23.00	28.00
1908 Motto (In God We Trust)	341,486	23.00	28.00
1908D No motto	210,000	23.00	28.00
1908D Motto	836,500	23.00	28.00
1908S Motto	59,853	25.00	35.00
1909	184,860	22.00	28.00
1909D	121,540	22.00	28.00
1909S	292,350	22.00	28 00
1910	318,704	22.00	28.00
1910D	2,356,640	22.00	28.00
1910S	811,000	22.00	28.00
1911	505,595	22.00	28.00
1911D	30,100	30.00	37.00
1911S	51,000	30.00	37.00
1912	405,083	22.00	28.00
1912S	300,000	22.00	28.00
1913	442,071	22.00	28.00
1913S	66,000	30.00	37.00
1914	151,050	22.00	28.00
1914D	343,500	22.00	28.00
1914S	208,000	22.00	28.00
1915	351,075	22.00	28.00
1915S	59,000	32.00	42.00
1916S	138,500	27.00	37.00
1920S	126,500	225.00	500.00
1926	1,014,000	22.00	28.00
1930S	96,000	450.00	950.00
1932	4,463,000	22.00	28.00
1933	312,500	400.00	1,000.00

DOUBLE EAGLES ($20.00 Gold Pieces)

(Coined for general circulation from 1850 to 1932, both dates inclusive. A specimen dated 1849 is in the Mint Collection.)

This series is not collected extensively by dates except by the more wealthy collectors due to the high face value. Most of the dates are not rare except in uncirculated or proof condition; 1883 is the rarest date as only 40 were coined. Proofs before 1890 are quite rare as only 25 to 35 pieces each year were struck in that condition. The last year of coinage, 1933, was not officially released.

Fine — LIBERTY complete and readable. Last seven crown jewels show wear. Hairlines worn.
Ex. Fine — Slight wear on curls and crown jewels. Tiny bagmarks.

	Quan. Minted	Fine	Ex. Fine
1849 (In U. S. Mint Collection)	1		
1850	1,170,261	$ 47.00	$ 80.00
1850O	141,000	65.00	82.00
1851	2,087,155	40.00	50.00
1851O	315,000	60.00	80.00
1852	2,053,026	43.00	55.00
1852O	190,000	60.00	77.00
1853	1,261,326	42.00	50.00
1853O	71,000	60.00	95.00
1854	757,899	42.00	50.00
1854O	3,250	150.00	250.00
1854S	141,468	47.00	60.00
1855	364,666	42.00	52.00
1855O	8,000	75.00	95.00
1855S	879,675	43.00	50.00
1856	329,878	42.00	52.00
1856O	2,250	150.00	250.00
1856S	1,189,750	42.00	50.00
1857	439,375	42.00	50.00
1857O	30,000	60.00	85.00
1857S	970,500	42.00	48.00
1858	211,714	43.00	52.00
1858O	35,250	50.00	75.00
1858S	846,710	42.00	51.00
1859	43,597	42.00	51.00
1859O	9,100	75.00	100.00
1859S	636,445	42.00	48.00
1860	577,670	42.00	48.00
1860O	6,600	85.00	115.00
1860S	544,950	42.00	50.00
1861	2,976,453	42.00	50.00

Prices listed for all gold coins are for choice specimens. Those grading less than the condition listed bring proportionately less.

DOUBLE EAGLES ($20.00 Gold Pieces)

	Quan. Minted	Fine	Ex. Fine
1861O	5,000	$ 85.00	$110.00
1861S	768,000	39.00	43.00
1862	92,133	39.00	43.00
1862S	854,173	39.00	43.00
1863	142,790	39.00	43.00
1863S	966,570	39.00	43.00
1864	204,285	39.00	43.00
1864S	793,660	39.00	43.00
1865	351,200	39.00	43.00
1865S	1,042,500	39.00	43.00
1866S No motto		150.00	300.00
1866 Motto	698,775	39.00	43.00
1866S Motto (all kinds)	842,250	39.00	43.00
1867	251,065	39.00	43.00
1867S	920,750	39.00	43.00
1868	98,600	39.00	43.00
1868S	837,500	39.00	43.00
1869	175,155	39.00	43.00
1869S	686,750	39.00	43.00
1870	155,185	39.00	43.00
1870CC	3,789	1,000.00	3,000.00
1870S	982,000	39.00	43.00
1871	80,150	40.00	44.00
1871CC	14,687	90.00	110.00
1871S	928,000	39.00	43.00
1872	251,880	39.00	43.00
1872CC	29,650	80.00	110.00
1872S	780,000	39.00	43.00
1873	1,709,825	39.00	43.00
1873CC	22,410	80.00	105.00
1873S	1,040,600	39.00	43.00
1874	366,800	39.00	43.00
1874CC	115,085	51.00	61.00
1874S	1,214,000	39.00	43.00
1875	295,740	39.00	43.00
1875CC	111,151	50.00	62.00
1875S	1,230,000	39.00	43.00
1876	583,905	39.00	43.00
1876CC	138,441	45.00	52.00
1876S	1,597,000	39.00	43.00
1877	397,670	39.00	43.00
1877CC	42,565	50.00	65.00
1877S	1,735,000	39.00	43.00
1878	543,645	39.00	43.00
1878CC	13,180	60.00	72.00
1878S	1,739,000	39.00	43.00
1879	207,630	39.00	43.00
1879CC	10,708	67.00	80.00
1879O	2,325	90.00	125.00
1879S	1,223,800	39.00	43.00
1880	51,456	39.00	43.00
1880S	836,000	39.00	43.00
1881	2,260	95.00	125.00
1881S	727,000	39.00	43.00

DOUBLE EAGLES ($20.00 Gold Pieces)

	Quan. Minted	Fine	Ex. Fine
1882	630	$125.00	$200.00
1882CC	39,140	50.00	65.00
1882S	1,125,000	39.00	43.00
1883 (Proofs only) Beware — removed mint mark	40	Proof	3,250.00
1883CC	59,962	50.00	62.00
1883S	1,189,000	39.00	43.00
1884 (Proofs only) Beware — removed mint mark	71	Proof	3,500.00
1884CC	81,139	50.00	62.00
1884S	916,000	39.00	43.00
1885	828	110.00	145.00
1885CC	9,450	60.00	80.00
1885S	683,500	39.00	43.00
1886	1,106	100.00	180.00
1887 (Proofs only) Beware — removed mint mark	121	Proof	1,500.00
1887S	283,000	39.00	43.00
1888	226,266	39.00	43.00
1888S	859,600	39.00	43.00
1889	44,111	43.00	50.00
1889CC	30,945	50.00	65.00
1889S	774,700	39.00	43.00
1890	75,995	39.00	43.00
1890CC	91,209	50.00	60.00
1890S	802,750	39.00	43.00
1891	1,442	75.00	90.00
1891CC	5,000	75.00	95.00
1891S	1,288,125	39.00	43.00
1892	4,523	55.00	72.00
1892CC	27,265	52.00	62.00
1892S	930,150	39.00	43.00
1893	344,339	39.00	43.00
1893CC	18,402	57.00	67.00
1893S	996,175	39.00	43.00
1894	1,368,990	39.00	43.00
1894S	1,048,550	39.00	43.00
1895	1,114,656	39.00	43.00
1895S	1,143,500	39.00	43.00
1896	792,663	39.00	43.00
1896S	1,403,925	39.00	43.00
1897	1,383,261	39.00	43.00
1897S	1,470,250	39.00	43.00
1898	170,470	39.00	43.00
1898S	2,575,175	39.00	43.00
1899	1,669,384	39.00	43.00
1899S	2,010,300	39.00	43.00
1900	1,874,584	39.00	43.00
1900S	2,459,500	39.00	43.00
1901	111,526	41.00	45.00
1901S	1,596,000	39.00	43.00
1902	31,254	50.00	60.00
1902S	1,753,625	39.00	43.00
1903	287,428	41.00	45.00
1903S	954,000	39.00	43.00
1904	6,256,797	39.00	43.00
1904S	5,134,175	39.00	43.00

DOUBLE EAGLES ($20.00 Gold Pieces)

	Quan. Minted	Fine	Ex. Fine
1905	59,011	$ 39.00	$ 43.00
1905S	1,813,000	39.00	43.00
1906	69,690	39.00	43.00
1906D	620,250	39.00	43.00
1906S	2,065,750	39.00	43.00
1907 Liberty	1,451,864	39.00	43.00
1907D Liberty	842,250	39.00	43.00
1907S Liberty	2,165,800	39.00	43.00

Fine — Wear evident on full length of right leg. Drapery at chest worn flat. Leaves beneath date worn. Eagle's wing tips worn noticeably.
Ex. Fine — Drapery lines on chest visible. Wear on right breast, knee and below. Eagle's feathers on breast and right wing are bold.

	Quan. Minted	Fine	Ex. Fine
1907 Flying eagle, MCMVII	11,250	200.00	350.00
1907 Flying eagle, 1907	361,667	45.00	52.00
1908 No motto	4,271,551	39.00	45.00
1908 Motto (In God We Trust)	156,359	39.00	45.00
1908D No motto	663,750	41.00	45.00
1908D Motto	349,500	41.00	45.00
1908S Motto	22,000	62.00	80.00
1909 9 over 8		70.00	95.00
1909 (All kinds)	161,282	40.00	44.00
1909D	52,500	41.00	45.00
1909S	2,774,925	40.00	44.00
1910	482,167	40.00	44.00
1910D	429,000	40.00	44.00
1910S	2,128,250	40.00	44.00
1911	197,350	40.00	44.00
1911D	846,500	40.00	44.00
1911S	775,750	40.00	44.00
1912	149,824	43.00	46.00
1913	168,838	41.00	43.00
1913D	393,500	41.00	43.00
1913S	34,000	60.00	70.00
1914	95,320	41.00	44.00
1914D	453,000	41.00	44.00
1914S	1,498,000	41.00	44.00
1915	152,050	41.00	44.00
1915S	567,500	41.00	44.00
1916S	796,000	41.00	44.00
1920	228,250	41.00	44.00
1920S	558,000	105.00	175.00

DOUBLE EAGLES ($20.00 Gold Pieces)

	Quan. Minted	Fine	Ex. Fine
1921	528,500	$300.00	$400.00
1922	1,375,500	41.00	44.00
1922S	2,658,000	75.00	100.00
1923	566,000	39.00	43.00
1923D	1,702,250	39.00	43.00
1924	4,323,500	39.00	43.00
1924D	3,049,500	43.00	47.00
1924S	2,927,500	150.00	200.00
1925	2,831,750	40.00	44.00
1925D	2,938,500	100.00	175.00
1925S	3,776,500	70.00	90.00
1926	816,750	41.00	44.00
1926D	481,000	250.00	350.00
1926S	2,041,500	150.00	200.00
1927	2,946,750	41.00	44.00
1927D	180,000	400.00	1,300.00
1927S	3,107,000	170.00	200.00
1928	8,816,000	39.00	43.00
1929	1,779,750	170.00	300.00
1930S	74,000	300.00	700.00
1931	2,938,250	280.00	550.00
1931D	106,500	350.00	700.00
1932	1,101,750	220.00	400.00
1933 Held from circulation	(445,500)		

COMMEMORATIVE COINS

The unique position occupied by Commemoratives in United States coinage is largely due to the fact that they are the only coins that have a real historical significance. No other coins bear any definite relation to historical events. It is the historical features of the Commemoratives which create interest among people who otherwise have little interest in coins.

Commemorative half dollars are considered for coinage by two committees of Congress — The Committee on Banking and Currency of the Senate, and the Committee on Coinage, Weights and Measures of the House. Congress is guided to a great extent by the reports of these committees when passing upon bills authorizing commemorative coins.

Memorial coins are issued either to commemorate special events, or to help pay for monuments or celebrations that commemorate historical persons, places or things.

A complete set of Commemorative half dollars comprises 48 types, and with the addition of mint mark varieties makes a total of 142 coins to the series.

No Commemorative coin was struck from 1940 to 1945.

COMMEMORATIVE SILVER COINS

In 1892, to commemorate the World's Columbian Exposition in Chicago, Congress authorized the coinage of a special half dollar and quarter dollar, thus starting a long line of United States commemorative coins. All commemorative coins have been distributed by private individuals or commissions; they paid the mint the face value of the coins and in turn sold the pieces at a premium to collectors. There are a few instances in which some of the very large issues were released in circulation by the commissions at face.

COMMEMORATIVE SILVER

Isabella, Lafayette, Alabama

Commemoratives is a series that is collected generally in uncirculated condition and the common varieties that have been circulated are practically unsaleable. Even the rare varieties are sold at great discount when in anything but mint state.

Due to their different designs and the events they commemorate this is a popular series and is worthy of the consideration of every American collector.

Commemorative totals are given as "quantity available." In many instances a portion of the total coinage has been melted. The figures given here represent the quantity of coins that are still in the hands of collectors and dealers.

		Quan. Available	Ex. Fine	Unc.
1893	Isabella Quarter	24,214	$27.50	$50.00

1900	Lafayette Dollar	36,026	35.00	65.00

1921	Alabama, 2 x 2 in field	6,006	20.00	50.00
1921	Same, No 2 x 2	59,038	17.50	37.50

COMMEMORATIVE SILVER
Albany, Antietam, Arkansas

	Quan. Available	Ex. Fine	Unc.
1936 Albany, New York	17,671	$17.50	$35.00

1937 Battle of Antietam 1862-1937	18,028	20.00	60.00

1935	Arkansas Centennial	13,012	
1935D	Same type, D mint	5,505	Set 21.00
1935S	Same type, S mint	5,506	
1936	Arkansas Centennial, same as 1935 — date 1936 on reverse	9,660	
1936D	Same type, D mint	9,660	Set 21.00
1936S	Same type, S mint	9,662	
1937	Arkansas Centennial, same as 1935	5,505	
1937D	Same type, D mint	5,505	Set 21.00
1937S	Same type, S mint	5,506	
1938	Arkansas Centennial, same as 1934	3,156	
1938D	Same type, D mint	3,155	Set 42.50
1938S	Same type, S mint	3,156	
1939	Arkansas, same as 1935	2,104	
1939D	Same type, D mint	2,104	Set 225.00
1939S	Same type, S mint	2,105	

COMMEMORATIVE SILVER
Bay Bridge, Boone

		Quan. Available	Ex. Fine	Unc.
1936S	San Fran.-Oak'd Bay Bridge, S mint.......	71,424	$7.50	$20.00

1934	Daniel Boone Bicentennial................	10,007	2.00	7.50
1935	Same type.............................	10,010	1.85	7.00
1935D	Same type, D mint.....................	5,005	3.50	9.00
1935S	Same type, S mint......................	5,005	3.50	9.00

1935	Daniel Boone Bicentennial, same as 1934 but small 1934 added on reverse......	10,008	2.00	7.00
1935D	Same type, D mint....................	2,003 Pair		225.00
1935S	Same type, S mint...................	2,004		
1936	D. Boone Bicentennial, same as 1934...	12,012	2.00	6.25
1936D	Same type, D mint....................	5,005	3.25	8.50
1936S	Same type, S mint...................	5,006	3.25	8.50
1937	D. Boone Bicentennial, same as 1934....	9,810		
1937D	Same type, D mint....................	2,506 Set		200.00
1937S	Same type, S mint...................	2,506		
1938	Daniel Boone, same as 1934...........	2,100		
1938D	Same type, D mint....................	2,100 Set		250.00
1938S	Same type, S mint...................	2,100		

COMMEMORATIVE SILVER
Bridgeport, California, Cincinnati, Cleveland

		Quan. Available	Ex. Fine	Unc.
1936	Bridgeport, Conn., Centennial........	25,015	$10.00	$24.00

| 1925S | California Diamond Jubilee.......... | 86,594 | 8.00 | 20.00 |

1936	Cincinnati Musical Center............	5,005 ⎫		
1936D	Same type, D mint....................	5,005 ⎬ Set		185.00
1936S	Same type, S mint....................	5,006 ⎭		

| 1936 | Cleveland, Great Lakes Exposition........ | 50,030 | 3.00 | 7.00 |

COMMEMORATIVE SILVER
Columbia, S.C., Columbian, Connecticut, Delaware

		Quan. Available	Ex. Fine	Unc.
1936	Columbia, S.C., Sesquicentennial	9,007 ⎫		
1936D	Same type, D mint	8,009 ⎬ Set		$60.00
1936S	Same type, S mint	8,007 ⎭		

| 1892 | Columbian Half | 950,000 | $ .90 | 3.00 |
| 1893 | Columbian Half | 1,550,405 | .75 | 2.50 |

| 1935 | Connecticut Tercentenary | 25,018 | 17.00 | 34.50 |

| 1936 | Delaware Tercentenary | 20,993 | 10.00 | 30.00 |

[111]

COMMEMORATIVE SILVER
Elgin, Gettysburg, Grant, Hawaiian

		Quan. Available	Ex. Fine	Unc.
1936	Elgin, Illinois, Centennial..................	20,015	$9.00	$28.00

1936	Battle of Gettysburg 1863-1938.............	26,928	13.50	30.00

1922	Grant Memorial, Small star in obv. field......	4,256	55.00	100.00
1922	Same, no star in obverse field.............	67,405	5.00	15.00

(Fake stars have flattened spot on reverse.)

1928	Hawaiian Sesquicentennial................	10,008	200.00	350.00

COMMEMORATIVE SILVER
Hudson, Huguenot, Iowa, Lexington

	Quan. Available	Ex. Fine	Unc.
1935 Hudson N. Y. Sesquicentennial..............10,008		$60.00	$170.00

1924 Huguenot-Walloon Tercentenary..........142,080	6.00	17.50

1946 Iowa Centennial........................100,057	6.00	12.00

1925 Lexington Concord Sesquicentennial.......162,013	3.50	7.00

COMMEMORATIVE SILVER
Lincoln, Long Island, Lynchburg, Maine

		Quan. Available	Ex. Fine	Unc.
1918	Illinois Centennial	100,058	$5.00	$16.50

| 1936 | Long Island Tercentenary | 81,826 | 4.50 | 11.00 |

| 1936 | Lynchburg, Va., Sesquicentennial | 20,013 | 9.00 | 27.50 |

| 1920 | Maine Centennial | 50,028 | 6.00 | 17.00 |

COMMEMORATIVE SILVER
Maryland, Missouri, Monroe, New Rochelle

		Quan. Available	Ex. Fine	Unc.
1934	Maryland Tercentenary...................	25,015	$9.00	$22.50

1921	Missouri Centennial, 2 ★ 4 in field..........	5,000	35.00	75.00
1921	Same, no 2 ★ 4 in field of obverse..........	15,428	30.00	70.00

1923S	Monroe Doctrine Centennial.............	274,077	4.00	10.00

1938	New Rochelle, N. Y. 1688-1938.............	15,266	17.50	47.50

COMMEMORATIVE SILVER
Norfolk, Oregon, Panama-Pacific

		Quan. Available	Ex. Fine	Unc.
1936	Norfolk, Va., Bicentennial	16,936	$14.00	$40.00

1926	Oregon Trail Memorial	47,955	2.00	6.50
1926S	Same type, S mint	83,055	1.75	6.25
1928	Oregon Trail Memorial, same as 1926	6,028	2.00	7.50
1933D	Ore. Trail Mem., same type, D mint	5,008	2.50	8.50
1934D	Ore. Trail Mem., same type, D mint	7,006	2.00	7.00
1936	Oregon Trail Memorial, same as 1926	10,006	2.00	6.75
1936S	Same type, S mint	5,006	3.00	8.00
1937D	Oregon Trail Mem., D mint, same as 1926	12,008	2.00	6.50
1938	Oregon Trail Mem., same as 1926	6,006 ⎫		
1938D	Same type, D mint	6,005 ⎬ Set		22.50
1938S	Same type, S mint	6,006 ⎭		
1939	Oregon Trail, same as 1926	3,004 ⎫		
1939D	Same type, D mint	3,004 ⎬ Set		70.00
1939S	Same type, S mint	3,005 ⎭		

1915S	Panama Pacific Exposition, S mint	27,134	22.50	55.00

COMMEMORATIVE SILVER
Pilgrim, Rhode Island, Roanoke, Robinson

		Quan. Available	Ex. Fine	Unc.
1920	Pilgrim Tercentenary....................	152,112	$2.25	$ 6.25
1921	Same type.............................	20,053	5.00	11.00

1936	Rhode Island Tercentenary........... 20,013 ⎫	
1936D	Same type, D mint................... 15,010 ⎬ Set	29.00
1936S	Same type, S mint................... 15,011 ⎭	

1937	Roanoke Island, N. C., 1587-1937......... 29,030	6.50	15.00

1936	Arkansas Centennial (Robinson)........... 25,265	7.00	16.00

COMMEMORATIVE SILVER
San Diego, Sesqui-Centennial, Spanish Trail, Stone Mountain

		Quan. Available	Ex. Fine	Unc.
1935S	San Diego, Calif.-Pac. Exp., S mint	70,132	$4.00	$13.00
1936D	San Diego, California-Pacific Expo., D mint, same as 1935	30,092	5.00	14.00

1926	Sesquicentennial of American Independence	141,120	3.75	14.00

1935	Old Spanish Trail 1535-1935	10,008	60.00	150.00

1925	Stone Mountain Memorial	1,314,709	2.00	4.50

COMMEMORATIVE SILVER

Texas, Vancouver, Vermont

		Quan. Available	Ex. Fine	Unc.
1934	Texas Centennial..................61,350		$3.00	$ 9.50
1935	Texas Centennial, same as 1934........9,994			
1935D	Same type, D mint..................10,007 Set			27.00
1935S	Same type, S mint..................10,008			
1936	Texas Centennial, same as 1934........8,911			
1936D	Same type, D mint...................9,039 Set			27.00
1936S	Same type, S mint...................9,064			
1937	Texas Centennial, same as 1934........6,571			
1937D	Same type, D mint...................6,605 Set			27.00
1937S	Same type, S mint...................6,637			
1938	Texas Centennial, same as 1934........3,780			
1938D	Same type, D mint...................3,775 Set			62.50
1938S	Same type, S mint...................3,816			

1925S	Fort Vancouver Centennial...............14,994	30.00	75.00

1927	Vermont Sesquicentennial (Bennington)....28,162	15.00	32.50

COMMEMORATIVE SILVER
Washington, B. T., Washington-Carver, Wisconsin

	Quan. Available	Unc.		Quan. Available	Unc.
1946 Booker T. Washington Memorial	1,000,546		1949	6,004	
1946D	200,113	Set $ 3.75	1949D	6,004	Set $20.00
1946S	500,279		1949S	6,004	
1947	100,017		1950	6,004	
1947D	100,017	Set 9.00	1950D	6,004	Set 20.00
1947S	100,017		1950S	512,091	
1948	8,005		1951	510,082	
1948D	8,005	Set 15.00	1951D	7,004	Set 17.50
1948S	8,005		1951S	7,004	

	Quan. Available	Unc.		Quan. Available	Unc.
1951 Washington-Carver	110,018		1953	8,003	
1951D	10,004	Set 12.00	1953D	8,003	Set 17.50
1951S	10,004		1953S	108,020	
1952	2,006,292		1954	12,006	
1952D	8,006	Set 17.50	1954D	12,006	Set 13.00
1952S	8,006		1954S	122,024	

	Quan. Available	Ex. Fine	Unc.
1936 Wisconsin Centennial	25,015	$ 7.50	$20.00

COMMEMORATIVE SILVER
York County

		Quan. Available	Ex. Fine	Unc.
1936	York County, Maine Centennial............	25,015	$ 6.00	$ 14.00

COMMEMORATIVE GOLD
Grant, Lewis & Clark, Louisiana Purchase

1922	Grant Memorial Dollar with star...........	5,016	115.00	245.00
1922	Grant Memorial Dollar without star.........	5,000	130.00	275.00

1904	Lewis and Clark Exposition Dollar.........	10,025	140.00	290.00
1905	Lewis and Clark Exposition Dollar.........	10,041	140.00	290.00

1903	Louisiana Purchase Jefferson Dollar........	17,500	32.00	70.00
1903	Louisiana Purchase McKinley Dollar........	17,500	32.00	70.00

COMMEMORATIVE GOLD
McKinley, Panama Pacific

		Quan. Available	Ex. Fine	Unc.
1916	McKinley Memorial Dollar	9,977	$30.00	$75.00
1917	McKinley Memorial Dollar	10,000	40.00	125.00

1915S	Panama Pacific Exposition Dollar	15,000	24.00	40.00

1915S	Panama Pacific Exposition $2.50	6,749	145.00	265.00

1915S	Panama Pacific $50 Round	483		4,000.00
1915S	Panama Pacific $50 Octagonal	645		3,000.00

COMMEMORATIVE GOLD
Sesquicentennial

	Quan. Available	Ex. Fine	Unc.
1926 Philadelphia Sesquicentennial $2.50	46,019	$25.00	$42.50

Round	Octagonal	Octagonal	Octagonal	Octagonal	Round

Quarter Dollar	Half Dollar	Dollar	Quarter Dollar	Half Dollar	Dollar

CALIFORNIA FRACTIONAL GOLD PIECES

California gold quarters, halves and dollars are of two kinds:

1. Originals — Made by private companies such as assayers and jewellers in both round and octagonal form. They were made during the gold boom. The denomination spelled DOL. or DOLLAR is found on the genuine pieces. Average premium prices are:

Quarter Dollar, Octagonal or Round	9.00	12.50
Half Dollar, Octagonal or Round	10.00	14.50
Dollar, Octagonal	30.00	50.00
Dollar, Round	175.00	250.00

2. Souvenir specimens do not have the words DOL. or DOLLAR and are worth considerably less than genuine specimens.

RECENT PROOF SETS
Cent — Nickel — Dime — Quarter — Half

1936	$360.00	1954	$9.00
1937	165.00	1955	8.50
1938	80.00	1956	4.75
1939	70.00	1957	3.50
1940	50.00	1958	7.00
1941	45.00	1959	3.00
1942 With both nickels,		1960 Small date	15.00
$44.00; one nickel	40.00	1960 Large Date	2.80
1950	62.50	1961	2.25
1951	31.00	1962	2.25
1952	19.00	1963	2.20
1953	13.00		

Proof coins were not struck from 1943-1949 inclusive.

Consult mint totals under cents, nickels, etc., in front of book for quantities of proof coins minted in the years listed above.

UNITED STATES FRACTIONAL CURRENCY

Issued by the United States government from 1862 to 1875 to relieve the shortage of minor coins. Damaged specimens are redeemable at their face value at the Treasury Department, Washington, D. C.

First Issue. With facsimiles of postage stamps of the period:

PERFORATED EDGES

	V. Fine	New
5¢	$4.50	$14.00
10¢	5.00	15.00
25¢	6.50	18.00
50¢	9.00	22.50

PLAIN EDGES

5¢	1.50	3.00
10¢	1.50	3.00
25¢	2.50	5.50
50¢	5.00	9.00

Second Issue. Bust of Washington in bronze oval:

5¢	1.25	3.00
10¢	1.25	3.00
25¢	2.00	4.00
50¢	2.50	5.00

Third Issue. Green Backs:

3¢ Washington	2.00	4.50
5¢ Clark	1.50	4.50
10¢ Washington	1.00	2.75
25¢ Fessenden	2.00	4.50
50¢ Justice	4.00	7.00
50¢ Spinner	2.50	5.00

RED BACKS

5¢	3.50	8.50
10¢	2.50	7.00
25¢	2.00	7.50
50¢ Justice	4.50	9.00
50¢ Spinner	3.75	8.50

Fourth Issue. Green Backs:

10¢ Liberty	1.00	2.50
15¢ Columbia	4.50	10.00
25¢ Washington	2.00	2.75
50¢ Lincoln	3.00	8.00
50¢ Stanton	2.00	3.50

Fifth Issue:

10¢ Meredith	1.00	2.00
25¢ Walker	1.00	2.25
50¢ Dexter	2.00	4.50
50¢ Crawford	2.00	3.50

COLONIAL COINAGE

The first "State" or Colonial coins struck in this country were the crude "NE Shillings" by the colony of Massachusetts. These pieces were followed by the famous Massachusetts "Pine Tree Shillings" which are dated 1652; this series also included sixpence and threepence pieces of 1662. Dealers buy the more popular Colonial coins at approximately the following prices (fine specimens):

NE Shilling..$250.00
Massachusetts Pine Tree and Oak Tree Shillings............$50.00 to 85.00
Pine Tree Sixpence ($35.00); Pine Tree Threepence.................$35.00
1787-8 Massachusetts Cents and Half Cents........................$7.00
1785 to 1788 Vermont Cents...........................$10.00 to 115.00
1786 to 1788 New Jersey Cents...........................$5.00 to 20.00
1785-1788 Connecticut Cents.............................$4.00 to 20.00
1773 Virginia Halfpenny..................................$4.00 to 4.50

A number of tokens were struck from 1783 to 1791 with the portrait of George Washington and some of these pieces are worth from $5.00 to $12.50, others are extremely rare.

U. S. COIN STANDARDS

Kinds and denomina-tions of coins	Diameter	Thickness	Standard or gross weight of coins	
	Inches	Inches	Oz. Troy	Grains
SILVER:				
Dollar..........	1.5	.114	.859375	412.5
Half-dollar......	1.205	.086	.401875	192.9
Quarter-dollar...	.955	.067	.200937	96.45
Dime..........	.705	.053	.080375	38.58
MINOR:				
Five-cent.......	.835	.078	.16075	77.16
One-cent........	.750	.062	.1	48.0

Kinds and denominations of coins	Weight toler-ance (above or below) on in-dividual pieces	Fineness	Fineness toler-ance on coinage ingots
	Grains	Thousandths	Thousandths
SILVER:			
Dollar.................	6.0	900	6
Half-dollar.............	4.0	900	6
Quarter-dollar..........	3.0	900	6
Dime..................	1.5	900	6
MINOR:			
Five-cent...............	3.0	75 percent copper; 25 per-cent nickel	Of nickel 25
One-cent...............	2.0	95 percent copper; 5 per-cent tin and zinc	Starting 1962-95 percent copper; 5 per-cent zinc

INDEX

COIN FOLDERS

A Convenient Method
for Housing Your Collection

Made in two tones of blue . . . printed in black and silver, giving a brilliant "Jewel Case" effect to your coin collection.

Made by WHITMAN   Size Folded 5¾" x 7½"

COMPLETE LIST OF STYLES
UNITED STATES

Large Cent — 1793 to 1825
Large Cent — 1826 to 1857
Indian-Eagle Cents — 1856 to 1909
Lincoln Head Cent — 1909 to 1940
Lincoln Head Cent — Starting 1941
Lincoln Memorial Cent — Starting 1959
Cents — Plain, no printing

Half Dime — 1794 to 1873
Shield Type Nickel — 1866 to 1883
Liberty Head Nickel — 1883 to 1913
Buffalo Nickel — 1913 to 1938
Jefferson Nickel — 1938 to 1961
Jefferson Nickel — Starting 1962
Nickels — Plain, no printing

Bust Type Dime — 1796 to 1837
Liberty Seated Dime — 1837 to 1862
Liberty Seated Dime — 1863 to 1891
Barber Dime — 1892 to 1916
Mercury Head Dime — 1916 to 1945
Roosevelt Dime — Starting 1946
Dimes — Plain, no printing

Liberty Seated Quarter — 1838 to 1865
Liberty Seated Quarter — 1866 to 1891
Barber Quarter — 1892 to 1905
Barber Quarter — 1906 to 1916
Lib. Standing Quarter — 1916 to 1930
Wash. Head Quarter — 1932 to 1945
Wash. Head Quarter — 1946 to 1959
Wash. Head Quarter — Starting 1960
Quarters — Plain, no printing

Lib. Seated Half Dollar — 1839 to 1850
Lib. Seated Half Dollar — 1851 to 1862
Lib. Seated Half Dollar — 1863 to 1873
Lib. Seated Half Dollar — 1873 to 1891
Barber Half Dollar — 1892 to 1903
Barber Half Dollar — 1904 to 1915
Lib. Standing Half Dollar — 1916 to 1936
Lib. Standing Half Dollar — 1937 to 1947
Ben. Franklin Half Dollar — Starting 1948
Halves — Plain, no printing

Morgan Dollar — 1878 to 1883
Morgan Dollar — 1884 to 1890
Morgan Dollar — 1891 to 1897
Morgan Dollar — 1898 to 1921
Peace Dollar — 1921 to 1935
Dollars — Plain, no printing

MISCELLANEOUS

Half Cent — 1793 to 1857
Silver Three Cent — 1851 to 1873
Two Cent — Nickel Three Cent — 1864 to 1889
Type Coins, Small Denominations
Type Coins, Large Denominations
20th Century Type Coins

CANADA

Large Cents — 1858 to 1920
Small Cents — Starting 1920
Silver Five Cents — 1858 to 1921
Nickels — 1922-1960
Nickels — Starting 1961
Dimes — 1858 to 1936
Dimes — Starting 1937
Quarters — 1858 to 1910
Quarters — 1911 to 1952
Quarters — Starting 1953
Halves — 1870 to 1910
Halves — 1911 to 1936
Halves — 1937-1960
Halves — Starting 1961
Silver Dollars — 1935 to 1957
Silver Dollars — Starting 1958
Quarters — Plain, no printing
Halves — Plain, no printing
Canada Coin Type Collection
Dollars — Plain, no printing

NEWFOUNDLAND

Cents & Half Cents — Newfoundland, New Brunswick, Nova Scotia and Prince Edward Island
Newfoundland 5¢ — 1865 to 1947
N. Brunswick 5-10-20¢ — 1862 to 1864
Newfoundland 10¢ — 1865 to 1947
Newfoundland 20-25¢ — 1865 to 1919
Newfoundland 50¢ — 1870 to 1919
Newfoundland Coin Type Collection

GREAT BRITAIN

Farthings — 1860 to 1901
Farthings — 1902 to 1936
Farthings — 1937 to 1956
Halfpennies — 1860 to 1901
Halfpennies — 1902 to 1936
Halfpennies — Starting 1937
Pennies — 1860 to 1880
Pennies — 1881 to 1901
Pennies — 1902 to 1929
Pennies — Starting 1930
Threepence Silver — 1838 to 1901
Threepence Silver — 1902 to 1945
Threepence Brass — Starting 1937
Sixpence — 1902 to 1936
Sixpence — Starting 1937
Shillings — 1902 to 1936
Shillings — 1937 to 1951
Shillings — Starting 1953

MEXICO

One Centavo — Starting 1905
Five Centavos — 1905 to 1955
Five Centavos — Starting 1954